WICKED PUDDINGS

By the same author

How To Boil An Egg

Uniform with this book

WICKED
PUDDINGS

Jan Arkless

RIGHT WAY

Typeset in 10/11pt Swiss 721 by Letterpart Ltd., Reigate, Surrey.

Printed and bound in Great Britain by Cox & Wyman Ltd., Reading, Berkshire.

The Right Way series is published by Elliot Right Way Books, Brighton Road, Lower Kingswood, Tadworth, Surrey, KT20 6TD, U.K. For information about our company and the other books we publish, visit our web site at www.right-way.co.uk

CONTENTS

For the ladies who walk, laugh and lunch,
but mainly for
Amy, Jillian, Joanne and Alicia
who tackle all puds with great enthusiasm,
and also for Ben
who'll be there with his spoon
as soon as he's big enough to manage one!

INTRODUCTION

All puddings are wicked – and some are more wicked than others, depending on how large a helping you have and how much cream you pour over it – but who cares!

There's no such thing as a prim and proper pudding (even a plain 'good for you' yoghurt produces a little frisson of pleasure when you eventually find the spoonful of fruit at the bottom of the carton), and we all know people who go weak at the knees at the mention of bread and butter pudding, treacle tart or rice pudding with skin on, let alone all those absolutely luscious and scrumptious cream, fruit and chocolate concoctions that look and taste so delicious.

Puddings have once again returned to favour – people are now being invited for 'Drinks and Puddings' instead of those early evening 'Drinks with Nibbles Cocktail Parties' where you're left wondering what to do next when the party ends about nine o'clock and you're still hungry! Dessert is now the 'in' course, rediscovered by all the best chefs in all the best restaurants, and appreciated by diners of all ages, whether eating out or enjoying a meal at home with family or friends. Listen to the buzz of conversation in any restaurant today as the menu is studied – 'I'm definitely going to have a pudding so I'll just take a small main course,' or 'Forget the starters, let's all have puddings instead with custard and cream, and maybe ice cream as well!' Yippee!!

I hope you enjoy this book and that it will bring back lovely memories of puds gone by, and perhaps introduce you to lots of wicked puddings you've not tried before.

1

FRUIT FOR ALL SEASONS

*Using fruit from the orchard,
garden and hedgerow.*

Ki's Apple Snow

Very light, delicious and a treat for slimmers or those like my son Chris, known as Ki, who dislike cream. Make and serve the same day as it will separate if left overnight.

NB This recipe contains raw egg and should not be given to very young children, pregnant women or elderly people.

Serves 4   *Preparation & cooking time: 25-30 minutes*

500g/1 lb cooking apples
2 tbsp water
1 tbsp lemon juice
50-100g/2-4 oz granulated sugar
2 egg whites

Peel and core apples, slice thinly and simmer gently in pan with water and lemon juice until soft (5-10 minutes).

Leave to cool slightly, then purée in a processor or liquidizer or mash with a fork until smooth.

Sweeten to taste.

Whip egg whites until very stiff, fold into apple purée, being careful not to burst the air bubbles.

Pile into a glass or china serving bowl, or into individual sundae dishes or large wine glasses, and chill until needed.

Delicious served with Mary's American Vanilla Cookies (see page 126).

For a more exotic taste, omit the lemon juice and cook the apples in dry white wine or cider instead of water.

Apple Sundae

Half fill four large wine glasses with Apple Snow, and carefully place a scoop of vanilla ice cream in the middle of each sundae. Top with a thin twist of lemon peel and serve immediately.

Raspberry or Strawberry Cream

The ultimate in simple but delicious desserts, perfect for a summer meal.

Serves 4   *Preparation time: 10 minutes*

500g/1 lb raspberries or strawberries or a mix of both
300ml/½ pint double cream, Greek yoghurt or crème
**   fraîche – any mixture according to taste**
25-50g/1-2 oz caster sugar (if needed)
Fresh mint or lemon balm leaves to decorate

Rinse fruit carefully, hull strawberries, pick fruit over well.

Save a few choice berries for decoration and mash the rest of the fruit gently with a fork – don't crush too much.

Sweeten to taste.

Whip cream until thick but not solid, mix in Greek yoghurt or crème fraîche if used and fold fruit into cream mixture.

Pour into a glass serving dish or individual dishes and chill in fridge until needed.

Decorate with the reserved berries and a few mint or lemon balm leaves and serve.

Strawberry or Raspberry Cones

An 'instant' spectacular dessert, super for informal parties or *al fresco* meals in the garden.

Wash and drain a small punnet of strawberries or raspberries. Put a deep layer of sugar in a deep glass serving dish. Take a pack of 'posh' rolled waffle ice cream cones, and fill each cone with either strawberry or raspberry cream, as above, or thickly whipped double cream flavoured with a few drops of vanilla essence. Top with a small, whole strawberry (or half a large one) or a whole raspberry and decorate each cone with a small, fresh mint leaf. Carefully stand the cones upright in the prepared dish of sugar. Serve at once.

Gooseberry Fool

Delicious as a summer dessert when fresh gooseberries are in season, or as a lovely taste of summer when made using fruit from the freezer during the winter. The elderflower gives a delicate flavour to the gooseberries.

Serves 4   *Preparation & cooking time: 30 minutes*

500g/1 lb gooseberries
1-2 tbsp water
1 small tsp elderflower syrup (optional)
50-125g/2-4 oz granulated sugar to taste
300ml/½ pint double cream
To serve: shortbread fingers or oatmeal biscuits

Wash gooseberries (no need to top and tail), and put into a pan with water and elderflower syrup (if used).

Simmer over a low heat for 8-10 minutes until soft, stirring occasionally.

Cool slightly, pour into a liquidizer or processor and blend for a few moments, then sieve to give a velvety smooth purée.

Sweeten to taste.

Whip cream until thick but not solid, and fold into the purée. Do not over mix; a few creamy swirls give a decorative effect.

Pour into a large serving dish or individual glasses, chill until needed, and serve with the shortbread or biscuits.

Rhubarb Fool

Lovely with fresh pink rhubarb when first in season.

Substitute rhubarb for gooseberries. Chop the rhubarb into 2.5cm/1 inch lengths before cooking, and proceed as for Gooseberry Fool, adjusting the sugar to taste.

Blackberry Mousse

A delicious late summer dessert using freshly gathered blackberries, or lovely any time of year using fruit from the freezer. You can vary the ratio of blackberries to apples according to availability.

Serves 4-6 depending on appetites   *Preparation & cooking time: 30 minutes*

500g/1 lb blackberries
500g/1 lb cooking apples
4-6 tbsp water
125-225g/4-8 oz granulated sugar, according to taste
1 envelope gelatine with 2 tbsp hot water
300ml/½ pint double cream or crème fraîche
A few fresh blackberries and mint leaves for decoration

Rinse blackberries, simmer gently in pan with 2 tbsp water for 5-10 minutes, until soft. Peel, core and thinly slice apples, put in a pan with 2-3 tbsp water and simmer gently for 5-10 minutes until soft.

Cool slightly, then liquidize blackberries and rub through a nylon sieve to give a seedless purée. Liquidize cooked apples until smooth, then mix into the blackberry purée and sweeten to taste.

Dissolve gelatine in 2 tbsp hot water (or as directed on the packet), and whip into the fruit mixture.

Whip cream, if used, until thick but not solid. Fold whipped cream or crème fraîche into fruit mixture, pour mousse into a serving dish and refrigerate until set.

Decorate with fresh blackberries and mint leaves and serve.

Quick Blackberry Ice Cream

Any leftover mousse can be frozen in individual ramekin dishes, and served frozen or slightly softened as an instant blackberry ice cream pudding.

Autumn Baked Apples

A quick and easy traditional pudding – very cheap to make if you have an apple tree in your garden, or generous neighbours with one!

Serves 4   *Preparation & cooking time: 40-60 minutes*

4 medium large cooking apples
4 heaped tsp sugar – granulated soft brown or demerara
    or use 4 dsp honey instead of sugar
4 dsp sultanas, raisins or mixed dried fruit
6-8 tbsp water, apple juice or cider

Heat the oven at 190°C/375°F/fan oven 170°C/gas 5-6.

Wash and core the apples. With a sharp pointed vegetable knife cut a circle around the middle of each apple, just through the skin, and place the apples in a greased ovenproof dish.

Mix chosen sugar or honey and dried fruit together, and carefully fill the centre of each apple. Pour just enough water, apple juice or cider into the dish to cover the base.

Cover dish loosely with a sheet of cooking foil, and bake in the moderate oven for 30 to 40 minutes until apples are tender and cooked right through.

Serve each apple with a little juice from the dish spooned over the top. All these baked apples are great served with vanilla ice cream.

Alternative fillings:

Persian Baked Apples	**Christmas Baked Apples**
4 tsp honey 2 dsp chopped dates 2 dsp chopped mixed nuts	4 tbsp mincemeat 1 dsp sherry
Cook in apple juice, sweet cider or sweet white wine.	Cook in red wine.

Summer Pudding

A glorious mixture of all the gorgeous red soft fruits that are available in the summer.

Serves 4-6   Prep. time: 20-30 minutes + chilling overnight

1kg/2 lb mixed soft red fruits – raspberries, blackberries, redcurrants, blackcurrants, red cherries and straw-berries – use whatever is available according to taste
100-225g/4-8 oz sugar
Approximately 8 slices white bread

Prepare fruit: Pick over raspberries, remove stalks from red and blackcurrants and stone cherries; leave strawberries for later. Rinse fruit, place in a large, thick-based pan. Rinse, then hull strawberries (this way you do not wash the juices away), halve large berries, but do not add to the fruit in the pan yet.

Cook fruit mixture over a low heat for 4-5 minutes, then add the strawberries and cook for a further 2-3 minutes, until the juices begin to run and the fruit is tender. Do not over cook, or the fruit will break up and the fresh fruit flavour will be lost. Stir in sugar to taste, being careful not to mash the fruit. Remove pan from the heat.

Line a 900ml/1½ pint pudding basin or soufflé dish with the bread – cut off the crusts, and fit a slice of bread neatly into the base of the basin or dish. Cut more slices into triangles or fingers and line the sides, overlapping bread slightly. Seal by pressing the slices together to leave no gaps in the mould.

Spoon the fruit into the bread mould to fill the dish, reserving a small cupful of juice. Cover fruit with a bread lid. Put a plate or saucer on top (it must fit inside the rim of the dish). Top plate with a 1kg/2 lb weight and chill overnight.

To serve: Unmould carefully onto a large serving dish, spoon over the reserved juice to cover any white bread patches. Delicious on its own or with Cornish cream, thick Chantilly Cream, crème fraîche or Greek yoghurt, according to taste.

Creamy Grilled Peaches

Use sweet, ripe fresh peaches or nectarines, or tinned peaches for these quick desserts.

Serves 4   *Preparation time: 10 minutes + 1 hour to chill*

4 large, ripe peaches or nectarines or 1 large can (425g) peach slices
300ml/½ pint double cream, crème fraîche or Greek yoghurt
100g/4 oz demerara sugar

Stone, peel and thinly slice fresh fruit, or drain canned fruit, and place in one layer in a shallow ovenproof dish.

Whip cream (if used) until thick but not too solid, and spread cream, crème fraîche or Greek yoghurt over top of fruit.

Chill in fridge until ready to serve.

Sprinkle sugar over fruit and place dish under a very hot grill until sugar melts to a lovely golden film. Serve at once.

Baked Peaches

Serves 4   *Preparation & cooking time: 20 minutes*

4 large fresh peaches or nectarines
4 tbsp soft brown sugar
8 tbsp water – or use less water and add brandy or sherry

Heat oven at 190°C/375°F/fan oven170°C/gas 5-6.

Rinse fruit, cut in half, remove stone and place in a shallow ovenproof dish, cut side uppermost.

Heat sugar and liquid(s) gently in a pan, then boil for 3-4 minutes to make a thin syrup. Pour over peaches in the dish.

Bake for 10 minutes until soft. Serve with lots of thick cream!

Brandy or Sherry Peaches

A refreshing finale to a summer dinner party.

Serves 6   *Preparation time: 15-20 minutes + chilling time*

300ml/½ pint water
100g/4 oz sugar
4 tbsp brandy or dry sherry
6 large peaches – use white peaches if available

Put water and sugar in a pan, heat gently until sugar is dissolved, then boil for 3-4 minutes to make a thin syrup.

Stir in brandy or sherry and leave to cool.

To skin peaches: Put peaches in a pan, cover with boiling water, leave for a few moments, then drain and put into cold water. The skins should now peel off thinly and easily.

Prick each peach all over with a long stainless steel fork or skewer, and stand peaches closely together in a serving dish just large enough to hold them all comfortably.

Pour syrup over peaches, covering fruit completely.

Cover dish with plastic film and chill for several hours.

Serve very cold, spooning the lovely boozy syrup over each peach as it is served.

Summer Fruit Salad

Fruit salad looks gorgeous served in a large, glass bowl.

Serves 6-8   *Preparation time: 30 minutes*

100g/4 oz granulated sugar
150ml/¼ pint water
150ml/¼ pint fruit juice (orange, apple, cranberry, etc.) or
  dry white wine

Use any mixture from the fruits listed below:
2 large, ripe, fresh peaches – peeled, stoned and sliced
2 large, ripe nectarines – peeled, stoned and sliced
1 green, eating apple – cored and sliced, leave peel on
1 red, eating apple – cored and sliced, leave peel on
Small bunch green and/or black seedless grapes –
  washed
Small punnet strawberries – washed, hulled and sliced
Handful red and/or white cherries – washed and stoned
Half a small melon – ogen, galia or honeydew – peeled,
  de-seeded and cut into large dice
Slice of watermelon – peeled and cut into large dice
Half a small pineapple – peeled, sliced and cubed
1 ripe mango (if liked, it has a strong flavour) – stoned,
  peeled and cubed
1-2 bananas – peeled, sliced and sprinkled with lemon juice
1-2 large, sweet, dessert oranges – peeled and seg-
  mented
2 kiwi fruit – peeled and sliced
A few mint or lemon balm leaves to garnish

Put sugar in a pan with water and fruit juice, or wine if used.
Heat gently until sugar is dissolved, then boil for 3-4 minutes
to make a thin syrup. Remove from heat and allow to cool.

Prepare chosen fruit as above and put into a serving bowl,
mixing fruit gently to look pretty. When syrup is cool, pour it
over the fruit and mix carefully. Refrigerate until needed.

Garnish with mint or lemon balm, and serve with a bowl of
cream and/or crème fraîche separately.

Nutty Fruit Crunch

A lovely way to enjoy fresh summer fruits – apricots, plums, damsons, peaches, nectarines or other stone fruits can be used when they are cheap and plentiful.

Serves 4   *Preparation & cooking time: 50-60 minutes*

500g/1 lb fruit – apricots, plums, damsons, peaches or
   nectarines
3-4 tbsp water
Sugar to taste, according to the chosen fruit
50g/2 oz butter
100g/4 oz fresh, malted, brown breadcrumbs – or use
   white bread if you prefer
½ tsp mixed spice, cinnamon or ground nutmeg
75g/3 oz demerara sugar
75g/3 oz chopped mixed nuts

Heat oven at 180°C/350°F/fan oven 160°C/gas 4-5.

Wash fruit, cut in half and remove stones – peel peaches if you prefer although the skins will soften during cooking.

Poach fruit gently in a very little water for 4-5 minutes, until softened. Stir in sugar to taste.

Spoon fruit into a pie dish, removing any stones that were missed earlier.

Melt butter in a clean pan, add breadcrumbs and chosen spice, then stir in demerara sugar and nuts and mix into the melted butter.

Spoon crumb mixture over the fruit, smooth with a fork.

Bake in the moderate oven for 30-40 minutes until the top is a pale golden brown.

Serve hot or cold, with thick whipped cream, crème fraîche or vanilla ice cream.

Boozy Poached Pears

Choose nice, large, even-sized pears for these recipes. The basic method of preparation is the same, but the pears can be cooked in different syrups to complement the rest of the meal.

Serves 4-6 – allow one pear per serving, but someone always wants a second helping!   *Prep. & cooking time:1½ hours*

6 large, equal-sized pears

Heat the oven at 170°C/325°F/fan oven150°C/gas 3-4. Wash, core and peel pears – use a vegetable knife or apple corer to remove core from base of pears, but leave stalk for decoration. It's easier to core pears before they are peeled. Stand pears in a deep, ovenproof dish, that is just large enough to hold them all close together.

Pears in White Wine

150ml/¼ pint white wine
150ml/¼ pint water
6 tbsp sugar
2 lemons

Pears in Red Wine

150ml/¼ pint red wine
150ml/¼ pint water
6 tbsp sugar
1 sherry glass port

Pears in Grenadine

150ml/¼ pint grenadine syrup – this is non-alcoholic
150ml/¼ pint water
6 tbsp sugar
1 lemon
½ tsp each of cloves, cinnamon and nutmeg

Put chosen wine or grenadine, water and sugar in a pan over a low heat, adding lemon rind and juice to the white wine or grenadine. Stir until sugar is dissolved, then allow to boil gently for 4-5 minutes to thicken syrup slightly. Stir port into red wine syrup, add spices to grenadine, then pour chosen syrup over pears in the dish so that it nearly covers them.

Cook in the low oven for about an hour, spooning the syrup over pears frequently, until pears are soft. Serve hot or cold in the syrup, with a bowl of whipped cream, crème fraîche or ice cream.

Peach Melba

A classic dessert, created for and named after Dame Nellie Melba, the Australian opera singer. It should be made with fresh peaches, but you can cheat and use canned fruit.

Serves 4   Prep. & cooking time: 15 minutes + cooling time

4 fresh peaches or canned peaches in syrup
175g/6 oz granulated sugar
300ml/½ pint water
Raspberry Satin Sauce using 225g/8 oz fruit – see page 120
150ml/¼ pint double cream or aerosol cream
Luxury Vanilla Ice Cream – see page 104
2 tbsp flaked almonds

Halve fresh peaches, remove stones and peel thinly.

Put sugar and water into a wide pan and bring to the boil, stirring until sugar has dissolved.

Carefully place peaches in the syrup, cut side up, spoon syrup over each fruit and leave simmering over a very low heat for about 5 minutes until just soft but not wrinkled or collapsing.

Take pan from heat, and leave peaches in the syrup until cold.

Prepare Raspberry Satin Sauce as on page 120.

Whip cream until stiff and put into a piping bag.

To serve: Use wide sundae glasses and place a scoop of ice cream into each dish.

Lift cold fresh peaches from pan using a slotted spoon or slice, or drain canned peaches, and arrange two peach halves either side of the ice cream.

Spoon Raspberry Sauce over the top and decorate with a large rosette of piped whipped cream or aerosol cream, and sprinkle with a few flaked almonds.

Serve at once.

Sunday Jelly

A bright, fruit jelly was once the centre piece of a good Sunday tea in many households, probably chosen to impress visitors at the meal. It's fun for children to make, and will keep them busy all morning as they wait for each layer of jelly to set. Make the jelly in a jelly mould and unmould to serve, or use a pretty glass dish and serve it from the dish.

Serves 6   Prep. time: all morning, as the jelly slowly sets!

1 × 135g pack lemon jelly
1 × 330g can mandarin oranges or 1 × 425g can peach slices in fruit juice
Small punnet strawberries
100g/4 oz seedless grapes (green, black or a mixture)
100g/4 oz cherries

Put jelly in measuring jug, add 300ml/½ pint boiling water and stir until dissolved. Drain juice from canned fruit, stir into jelly and make up to 600ml/1 pint with cold water. Leave to cool but not set while you prepare the fruit.

Wash and hull strawberries, cut in half. Wash grapes, wash and stone cherries, drain well. Reserve some fruit to decorate.

Pour a thin layer of jelly over the base of the dish or mould and put in fridge or freezer. When set, arrange some of the prepared fruit over base of dish to form an attractive pattern dipping each piece in liquid jelly first. Cover carefully with jelly and chill again.

When firm add another layer of fruit and jelly as before, being careful to make the pattern look good on the sides of the dish or mould where the fruit will be seen. Chill until firm.

Add final layer of fruit, cover with jelly and chill until set.

Unmould by standing mould in hot water for a few seconds, cover with a plate and turn out, or serve in the glass dish.

Decorate with reserved fruit and piped whipped cream, or serve with a dish of thick cream.

Ruby Fruit Jelly for Grown Ups!

Serious jelly – the port gives the fruit a lovely flavour!

Serves 4-6   Preparation time: 10 minutes + setting time

1 × 135g pack raspberry or strawberry jelly
1 × 425g can raspberries
150ml/¼ pint approximately port wine
1 small punnet fresh strawberries

Put jelly into a measuring jug, add 300ml/½ pint boiling water, and stir until dissolved.

Drain raspberries, stir juice into jelly, then make jelly up to 600ml/1 pint with port. Leave to cool slightly.

Wash and hull strawberries, and cut into slices, saving a few small berries for decoration.

Stir fruit into jelly, being careful not to break up raspberries.

Rinse and drain a 750ml/1¼ pint jelly mould, basin or glass serving dish and pour in jelly mixture. Leave to set in fridge for several hours or overnight.

Unmould jelly by standing mould in hot water for a few seconds, cover with a pretty serving plate and turn out, or serve in the glass dish if you prefer.

Serve decorated with reserved fruit and a few tiny fresh mint leaves if available.

Plum and Almond Flan

The light whisked sponge flan complements the fresh fruit to make a lovely summer pud.

Serves 4-6   *Preparation & cooking time: 1 hour*

Sponge case: **3 eggs**
75g/3 oz caster sugar
½ tsp vanilla essence
75g/3 oz plain flour – sieved

Topping: **500g/1 lb sweet, ripe, golden plums**
3 tbsp fresh orange juice or brandy, to taste
1 tbsp granulated sugar
4 tbsp apricot jam
25g/1 oz toasted flaked almonds
150ml/¼ pint double or whipping cream
2 tsp caster sugar

Heat oven at 180°C/350°F/fan oven 160°/gas 4-5. Well grease a 20cm/8 in sponge flan tin, and line the centre with cooking parchment or greased greaseproof paper.

Beat eggs, sugar and vanilla in a large bowl with a whisk or electric mixer until thick and creamy – when you can write your initial on the mixture when lifting the whisk it's thick enough.

Fold flour into mixture a spoonful at a time and pour into tin.

Bake in moderate oven for 15-20 minutes until springy and golden. Remove from oven, cool slightly, then loosen edges with a knife and turn out onto a wire tray to cool completely.

Wash, halve and stone plums, put in bowl cut side up. Mix orange juice or brandy with granulated sugar and pour over plums. Brush top and sides of flan with 2 tbsp warm jam and roll flan in almonds to coat top and sides. Put on serving dish.

Whip cream with sugar until stiff. Drain plums, spoon syrup over base of flan and cover with whipped cream. Arrange plums on top of cream, cut side down. Warm rest of jam with 1-2 tsp water to thin it down, and spoon over tops of plums. Serve at once.

2

SCHOOL DAY DREAMS

*Dream on –
this is what real puddings are made of!*

Roly Poly Pudding

A light, suet crust pastry roll that can be filled with jam, syrup or fruit as you wish, and served with custard or a pouring sauce to make a lovely filling pudding on a cold winter day.

Serves 6   *Preparation & cooking time: 1 hour*

225g/8 oz self-raising flour
¼ tsp salt
100g/4 oz shredded vegetarian suet
8-9 tbsp cold water
Filling of choice – see below

Heat oven at 200°C/400°F/fan oven 180°C/gas 6-7.

Make pastry: Put flour, salt and suet in a bowl and mix well.

Add water gradually, mixing in with a knife to make a soft dough, and knead pastry lightly into a ball.

Roll out on a floured surface to an oblong 30 × 20cm/12 × 8 in. Spread with chosen filling, leaving a 2cm/1 in edge all round. Brush edges with water and roll pudding up from the shorter edge, like a Swiss roll.

Press and seal edges and lift carefully onto a baking sheet, with the join underneath. Bake for 35-40 minutes until crisp and golden.

Serve hot with custard or a store cupboard sauce – see page 122.

Fillings:
4-5 heaped tbsp jam, marmalade, syrup or lemon curd

Apple: Peel, core and thinly slice 1-2 cooking apples, spread over pastry and sprinkle with 2 tbsp granulated sugar.

Crunchy Nutty Apple: Spread pastry with apple slices as above, then sprinkle with 2 tbsp demerara sugar, 1 tbsp chopped mixed nuts and ½ tsp cinnamon or mixed spice.

Mincemeat: Spread pastry with 4-5 tbsp mincemeat.

Spotted Dick

Spotted Dick (or Spotted Richard as offered on the menu of a lovely Cotswolde tea shoppe) is often the first pud that springs to mind when people recall their favourite childhood pudding, so I thought I'd better include it – and it's delicious anyway!

Serves 6   *Preparation & cooking time: 2-2½ hours*

100g/4 oz plain flour
¼ tsp salt
2 level tsp baking powder
100g/4 oz fresh white breadcrumbs
100g/4 oz vegetarian suet
100g/4 oz granulated sugar
100g/4 oz seedless raisins – or any dried fruit as you prefer
2 eggs
150ml/¼ pint milk

Well butter a 1 litre/2 pint basin. Sieve flour, salt and baking powder into a bowl. Mix in breadcrumbs, suet and sugar and raisins or dried fruit. Beat eggs and stir into flour mixture, adding enough milk to make a soft dropping consistency (drops easily off the spoon).

Spoon into basin, cover with greased greaseproof paper and foil (or use a basin with a tight fitting lid), put in a steamer and cook over well simmering water for about 2 hours – refill pan with boiling water as needed – see page 30.

Remove from steamer, and tip onto a serving dish. Serve with custard and/or Sticky Syrup Sauce – see page 122.

Lemon and Raisin Pudding

Make as above with the following changes:

Put 2-3 tbsp lemon curd at the bottom of the greased basin.
Add grated rind of 2 lemons with the bread crumbs.
Stir 2 tbsp lemon juice into the mixture with the eggs.

Serve with custard or Charlbury Lemon Sauce (see page 122).

Autumn Steamed Suet Pudding

Lovely and warming on a cold foggy day. A light suet crust pudding bursting with garden fruits, either fresh or from the freezer, to remind us of summer days that will come again.

Serves 4-6
Preparation time: 20 minutes   *Cooking time: 2½-3 hours*

225g/8 oz suet pastry – see page 26
500g/1 lb cooking apples
225g/8 oz blackberries or red currants
100g/4 oz granulated or demerara sugar – to taste

Grease a 1 litre/2 pint basin, find steamer and boil kettle.

Make suet pastry and roll out on a floured surface into a circle about 0.5cm/¼ in thick, large enough to line the basin. Cut out one quarter of the circle, and roll this piece into a smaller round to make the pudding lid, and line the basin with the larger piece of pastry.

Peel, core and slice apples, rinse blackberries or red currants and fill basin with layers of fruit and sugar. Dampen edges of pastry, cover with pastry lid and pinch edges together neatly and seal tightly. Cover top with greased pleated greaseproof paper and foil and steam or boil for 2½-3 hours – see page 30.

When cooked, take basin from pan and leave for 5 minutes. Remove foil and paper and turn onto a warm serving dish. Serve at once with warm custard or cream.

Rhubarb Pudding

Use 750g/1½ lb rhubarb, cut in 3cm/1 in lengths. Sprinkle layers of fruit with a little ground ginger.

Gooseberry Pudding

Use 750g/1½ lb gooseberries, topped and tailed. Sprinkle layers of fruit with a little grated cinnamon or nutmeg.

Nora's Magic Chocolate Pudding

Highly recommended by my friend Nora! Fun to make, as the runny cocoa mixture poured over the top of the unbaked pud magically turns into a fudgy chocolate sauce underneath the gooey chocolate pudding. Wow!

Serves 4-6   *Preparation & cooking time: 1-1¼ hours*

125g/4 oz self-raising flour
50g/2 oz granulated sugar
50g/2 oz plain cooking chocolate, melted
50g/2 oz butter, melted
150ml/¼ pint milk
½ tsp vanilla essence

Sauce:
100g/4 oz soft brown sugar
3 tbsp cocoa
300ml/½ pint boiling water

Heat oven at 180°C/350°F/fan oven 160°C/gas 4-5.

Well butter a 900ml/1½ pint ovenproof dish.

Put flour and sugar into a mixing bowl.

Stir in melted chocolate, melted butter, milk and vanilla essence and beat well to make a thick runny batter.

Pour into prepared dish.

Make sauce: Mix together soft brown sugar and cocoa, stir in the boiling water and pour sauce over top of pudding.

Bake in the moderate oven for 40-45 minutes, until the sponge rises like magic above the chocolate fudge sauce.

Serve warm, with whipped cream (beat in a little sweetened drinking chocolate powder to make chocolate cream if you prefer), and/or vanilla or chocolate ice cream.

Steamed Sponge Puddings

Use this basic recipe to make a wide variety of lovely sponge puddings, adding chocolate, syrup, jam, lemon, dried fruits etc., as you wish. The puds can all be steamed or boiled, but if you have an actual steamer it is easier.

Serves 4-6
Preparation time: 15 minutes   *Cooking time: 1½ hours*

100g/4 oz soft margarine or butter
100g/4 oz caster sugar
2 eggs – well beaten
½ tsp vanilla essence
100g/4 oz self-raising flour
1 tsp baking powder
1-2 tbsp milk to mix if needed

Well grease a 1 litre/2 pint pudding basin and find the steamer!

Put fat, sugar, eggs, vanilla essence, flour and baking powder into a bowl or mixer, and beat well until pale, soft and creamy. Add extra ingredients – see suggestions opposite – adding milk if needed to make a soft mixture that will just drop off a spoon.

Spoon mixture into basin, cover top with pleated greased greaseproof paper (pleat the paper to allow for the pud to rise), and tie firmly with string or a rubber band. Cover top loosely with foil and put basin into steamer above a large saucepan, or put pudding into the saucepan if it is to be boiled.

Pour boiling water into saucepan, bring back to the boil and simmer pudding briskly for 1½ hours, topping up pan with boiling water as needed during cooking. If pudding is standing in the pan to boil, make sure water does not reach the foil lid and do not let the pan boil dry.

When pudding is well risen and cooked, carefully take basin from steamer or pan (avoiding the very hot steam), remove the foil and greaseproof paper, and turn the hot pudding out onto a warm serving dish. Serve with appropriate sauce, either poured over pudding or served separately, and/or custard, cream or crème fraîche.

Steamed Sponge Puddings using the basic recipe

Yummy Chocolate Pudding

Use soft brown sugar instead of caster sugar. Add 1 heaped tbsp cocoa with the flour. Stir 100g/4 oz chocolate chips into the creamed mixture. Serve with Hot Chocolate Sauce – see page 116.

Syrup Sponge Pudding (Treacle Pud!)

Put 3-4 tbsp golden syrup into basin before the pudding mix. Use soft brown or white sugar as preferred. Serve with Sticky Syrup Sauce – see page 122.

Jam or Marmalade Sponge Pudding with Coconut

Put 3-4 tbsp jam or marmalade into basin before the pudding mix. Add 2 tbsp desiccated coconut to creamed mixture (optional). Serve with Jam or Marmalade Sauce – see page 122.

Lemon Sponge Pudding

Put 3-4 tbsp lemon curd into basin before the pudding mix. Add grated rind of 2 lemons with the flour. Stir 1 tbsp lemon juice into the creamed mixture. Serve with Charlbury Lemon Sauce – see page 122.

Raisin and Ginger Sponge Pudding

Add 1 tsp ground ginger with the flour. Stir 100g/4 oz raisins (or sultanas) into the creamed mixture. Serve with Sticky Syrup Sauce – see page 122.

Cherry Sponge Pudding

Rinse 100g/4 oz glacé cherries in warm water, drain, cut into halves or quarters and stir into the creamed mixture. Serve with Strawberry or Raspberry Jam Sauce – see page 122.

Pineapple Sponge Pudding

Drain a small 200g can pineapple pieces, and stir into the creamed mixture, adding a little of the pineapple juice to the mixture if needed. Serve with Pineapple Sauce – see page 121.

Stucky Toffee Pudding

Yummy, delicious and definitely st*u*cky!

Serves 6 generously   *Prep. & cooking time: about 1 hour*

175g/6 oz stoned dates
300ml/½ pint boiling water
1 tsp bicarbonate of soda
50g/2 oz butter – softened not melted
175g/6 oz soft pale brown sugar
2 eggs
½ tsp vanilla essence
175g/6 oz self-raising flour

Topping: **100g/4 oz demerara or soft dark brown sugar**
            100g/4 oz butter
            4 tbsp golden syrup
            4 tbsp double cream

Heat oven at 180°C/350°F/fan 160°C/gas 4-5, and well butter a 25 × 20cm/10 × 8 in, about 3cm/1½ in deep, baking tin.

Chop dates, put in a pan with the water, bring to the boil and simmer for 2-3 minutes until dates soften. Mix in bicarbonate (it will fizz), stir and put mixture aside.

Put butter and sugar in a bowl and beat until pale and creamy. Whisk eggs and vanilla together, and beat into butter mixture.

Fold in flour and mix in dates and water to make a thick batter.

Pour into prepared tin, and bake for 30-40 minutes.

Make the sauce while pud is cooking: Put sugar, butter and syrup into a pan and melt over a gentle heat, stirring until all the ingredients have dissolved. Stir in cream, mix well and simmer for a few minutes while sauce thickens.

When pudding is risen and firm, remove from oven and allow to cool for a few minutes in the tin.

Turn out onto a warm serving dish and serve with the sauce poured over the top, adding a dollop of ice cream, thickly whipped cream or custard if really self-indulgent!

Pineapple Upside Down Pudding

A quick-to-make baked sponge pudding, always fun to turn out and find the lovely sticky fruit 'topping' underneath.

NB Any canned fruit can be used for the topping: apricot, pear or peach halves or mandarin slices are all very nice.

Serves 4-6   *Preparation & cooking time: about 1¼ hours*

Topping:
3-4 tbsp golden syrup
Small, 227g can pineapple slices
A few glacé cherries
100g/4 oz butter
100g/4 oz demerara sugar

Pudding:
100g/4 oz soft margarine
100g/4 oz caster sugar
100g/4 oz self-raising flour
2 beaten eggs
A little pineapple juice if needed

Heat oven at 190°C/375°F/fan oven 170°C/gas 5-6. Well butter a 20cm/8 in sponge sandwich tin, and spoon golden syrup over the base.

Drain pineapple, saving the juice, and arrange in a pattern with halved cherries on top of the syrup. Stir butter and demerara sugar in a pan over a low heat until melted, and pour carefully over the fruit.

Put margarine, sugar, flour and beaten eggs in a bowl and beat well with a mixer or wooden spoon for 3-4 minutes until mixture will just drop off a spoon, adding a little pineapple juice if needed. Spoon cake mix over fruit and smooth top.

Bake for 25-30 minutes, until well risen, firm and golden brown. Remove from oven and leave to stand for 5 minutes.

Turn out, upside down, onto a warm serving plate, and serve with Pineapple Sauce – see page 121 – and/or cream.

Eve's Pudding

Traditionally a delicious apple filling with a baked sponge topping, but any pie fruit can be used when in season.

Serves 4-6   *Preparation & cooking time: about 1 hour*

Topping: **100g/4 oz soft margarine or butter**
100g/4 oz caster sugar
2 eggs, beaten
½ tsp vanilla essence
100g/4 oz self-raising flour
1 tsp baking powder
1-2 tbsp milk

Filling: **500g/1 lb cooking apples**
75-100g/3-4 oz granulated sugar to taste

A little caster sugar for dredging the top

Heat oven at 190°C/375°F/fan oven 170°C/gas 5-6 and butter a 1 litre/2 pint ovenproof dish or deep pie dish.

Put all the topping ingredients, except milk, into a bowl or mixer and beat well until pale and creamy, adding milk if needed to make a soft mixture that will just drop off a spoon.

Peel, core and slice apples thinly, put into dish and mix in the sugar to taste.

Spoon sponge topping over apples, and smooth down gently. Bake for 35-40 minutes until sponge is risen, firm and brown. Dredge with caster sugar and serve hot with custard or cream.

Adam's Pudding

Make sponge topping as above, but omit vanilla essence and add ½ tsp almond essence with the eggs.

Add 75g/3 oz sultanas or seedless raisins with the apples and sweeten fruit with demerara sugar instead of white sugar.

Bake as above, but dredge the top with icing sugar and serve hot with thick cream flavoured with a little brandy or whisky.

Apple Crumble

Use any pie fruit to make a delicious crumble, but a sugary apple crumble, served with custard or cream, is hard to beat.

Serves 4-6   *Preparation & cooking time: about 1 hour*

Topping: **175g/6 oz plain flour**
75g/3 oz granulated sugar
75g/3 oz soft margarine or butter

Filling: **500g/1 lb cooking apples**
100g/4 oz granulated sugar – or to taste

Heat oven at 200°C/400°F/fan oven 180°C/gas 6-7.

Put flour and sugar in a bowl, add margarine or butter cut into small pieces, and rub together with fingertips until mixture looks like breadcrumbs – if using a processor follow the manufacturer's instructions.

Peel, core and thinly slice apples, put into a 1 litre/2 pint deep pie dish and mix in sugar to taste. Spoon topping over fruit and smooth down lightly with a fork.

Stand dish on a baking tray and cook for 30-35 minutes until fruit is soft and crumble is a lovely golden brown. Serve warm with custard, cream or crème fraîche.

Use any fruit filling as suggested for fruit pies – see page 91 – and top with any of the crumble toppings listed below, rubbed into 75g/3 oz soft margarine or butter.

Wholewheat Topping
Use 175g/6 oz wholewheat flour instead of plain flour and 75g/3 oz soft brown sugar instead of granulated sugar.

Scottish Oat Topping
75g/3 oz plain or wholemeal flour
75g/3 oz porridge oats or rolled oats
75g/3 oz demerara sugar

Crunchy Nut Crumble
Add 50g/2 oz chopped mixed nuts to any of the toppings.

Brown Betty

Traditionally made with apples, but delicious with rhubarb, apricots, gooseberries, plums or other fresh fruit in season.

Serves 4-6   *Preparation & cooking time: 1 hour*

500g/1 lb cooking apples
Grated rind and juice of 1 lemon
100g/4 oz fresh white breadcrumbs – or brown if preferred
100g/4 oz sugar – granulated or demerara
75-100g/3-4 oz butter

Heat oven at 190°C/375°F/fan oven 170°C/gas 5-6, and well butter a 1 litre/2 pint deep pie dish or ovenproof dish.

Peel, core and slice apples, and mix with the lemon juice. Mix breadcrumbs, sugar and lemon rind.

Put alternate layers of crumbs and apples into the dish, with the crumb mixture at bottom and top, dotting each crumb layer well with butter.

Dot top with butter, and bake for 35-40 minutes until brown. Serve warm with custard or thick cream.

Apple Charlotte

Use the Brown Betty recipe. Add 100g/4 oz vegetarian suet and omit the butter. Prepare as above, mixing the vegetarian suet with the breadcrumbs and sugar, before putting alternate layers in the dish with the apples.

Spicy Apple and Sultana Betty or Charlotte

To either recipe add:

100g/4 oz sultanas or seedless raisins
¼ tsp mixed spice, cinnamon or freshly grated nutmeg

Mix dried fruit and spices and sprinkle over each layer of apples when putting layers of apples and crumbs in the dish.

Spicy Apple Cake

Although baked in a cake tin, this is a delicious dessert which can be eaten warm or cold with cream or Chantilly Crème.

Serves 6-8   *Preparation & cooking time: 1-¼ hours*

2 eggs
100g/4 oz soft pale brown sugar
½ tsp vanilla essence
100g/4 oz butter, melted
175g/6 oz self-raising flour
1 tsp baking powder
1 tsp each mixed spice and cinnamon
Sprinkle freshly grated nutmeg
350g/12 oz cooking apples
50g/2 oz sultanas – optional
2 tbsp soft brown sugar and 1 tsp cinnamon for dredging

Heat oven at 190°C/375°F/fan oven 170°C/gas 5-6, and well butter a 20-22cm/8-9 in spring form tin.

Put eggs, sugar, vanilla essence in a bowl or mixer with the melted butter, and beat well until frothy and creamy.

Sieve flour, baking powder and spices together in another bowl, and then fold carefully into egg mixture, using a metal spoon to mix.

Peel, core and slice apples.

Spoon about half the cake mixture into the prepared tin and smooth evenly over the base. Spread apple slices on top and sprinkle with sultanas if used. Spoon remaining cake mix over the fruit – it will be a bit uneven but will smooth out as the cake cooks.

Bake for 40-45 minutes until risen, firm and golden brown.

Cool slightly, then remove from tin onto a serving plate and dredge with cinnamon sugar. Serve warm or cold with Chantilly Crème – see page 124 – thick pouring cream or crème fraîche.

Baked Orange and Lemon Pudding

When the pudding is served, a lovely fruit sauce is found hidden beneath the sponge topping.

Serves 4-6   *Preparation & cooking time: about 1 hour*

50g/2 oz softened butter
100g/4 oz caster sugar
1 large lemon and 1 large orange – rind and juice
2 eggs
50g/2 oz plain flour
150ml/¼ pint milk

Heat oven at 180°C/350°F/fan oven 160°C/gas 4-5.

Well butter a 900ml/1½ pint soufflé or deep ovenproof dish.

Put butter and sugar with grated lemon and orange rind, into a bowl or mixer and whisk together, gradually beating in the lemon and orange juice.

Separate eggs and beat yolks into mixture a little at a time.

Gradually fold in the flour and milk and mix together gently.

Whip egg whites until stiff but not solid, and fold into sponge mixture with a metal spoon.

Pour mixture into baking dish and stand dish on a baking tray.

Bake for 35-45 minutes until firm, well risen and golden brown.

Serve hot with pouring cream or vanilla ice cream, or cold with a bowl of thickly whipped double cream.

Raspberry Pudding

Put 225g/8 oz sweet fresh raspberries into the dish before topping with the orange and lemon pudding mixture.

Bake and serve as above – it's absolutely delicious!

3

DRINKA PINTA MILKA DAY

*So delicious that it's surprising these puddings
are amazingly good for bones, teeth and
growing children!*

Creamy Rice Pudding – with skin on!: 40
Lemon Rice Pudding: 40
Chocolate Rice Pudding: 40
Raisin Rice: 40
Tapioca Pudding: 40
Old-Fashioned Semolina or Sago Pudding: 41
Fluffy Semolina or Sago: 41
Crème Caramel: 42
Egg Custard Tart: 43
Queen's Pudding: 44
Chocolate Queen's Pudding: 44
Magic Honeycomb Mould: 45
Bread and Butter Pudding: 46
Magic Islands: 47
Pancakes: 48
Traditional Lemon Pancakes: 49
Syrup Pancakes: 49
Crunchy Honey and Walnut Pancakes: 49
Chocolate Pancakes: 49
Jammy Pancakes: 49
Fruity Pancakes: 49
Christmas Time Pancakes: 49
Crêpes Suzette: 50

Creamy Rice Pudding – with skin on!

A proper rice pudding, creamy and delicious. Only takes a few minutes to prepare and can then be left to its own devices in a low oven to cook slowly until needed. A larger pud is no more trouble to prepare but will take longer to cook.

Serves 3-4   *Preparation & cooking time: 1½-2 hours*
                     (allow 3-4 hours for a double size or larger pudding)

75g/3 oz pudding (round Carolina) rice
50g/2 oz granulated sugar
600ml/1 pint milk – full cream milk is nicest!
150ml/¼ pint pouring cream or evaporated milk
25g/1 oz butter
Large pinch grated nutmeg or mixed spice

Heat oven to 170°C/325°F/fan oven 150°C/gas 3-4. Well butter a 1 litre/2 pint deep ovenproof dish.

Put rice, sugar, milk and cream into dish and stir well. Dot with butter, sprinkle with grated nutmeg or mixed spice. Bake in the low oven until rice is soft and the skin is brown.

Serve warm with a bowl of cream, soft vanilla ice cream – or with a spoonful of strawberry jam if you must!!

Lemon Rice Pudding
Add grated rind of 1 lemon with the sugar.

Chocolate Rice Pudding
Add 50g/2 oz grated cooking chocolate with the sugar.

Raisin Rice – my father's favourite
Add 50g/2 oz washed raisins (or currants or sultanas) with the sugar.

Tapioca Pudding – the 'Frog-spawn Pudding' of school dinner days!
Substitute tapioca for pudding rice and prepare as above.

Old-Fashioned Semolina or Sago Pudding

You either love it or loathe it, but this really smooth pudding, served on its own or with stewed, fresh or canned fruit, fruit compote or the old-favourite red or yellow jam, is delicious.

Serves 3-4   Preparation & cooking time: 30-40 minutes

750ml/1¼ pint milk – full cream or semi-skimmed
50g/2 oz semolina or sago
50g/2 oz granulated sugar
Thinly pared rind of 1 lemon or a little grated nutmeg

Heat oven to 170°C/325°F/fan oven 150°C/gas 3-4. Well butter a 1 litre/2 pint deep pie dish.

Heat milk gently in a large, rinsed pan (with lemon rind if used) until milk is moderately hot.

Sprinkle semolina or sago into milk, whisking or stirring until milk comes to the boil.

Reduce heat, add sugar, and simmer for 5 minutes, stirring well.

Pour into buttered dish, sprinkle with nutmeg if used, and bake in low oven for 20-30 minutes until thick and creamy.

Remove lemon rind if used, and serve with stewed or fresh fruit in season (cooked plums, rhubarb or apples, crushed raspberries or strawberries), canned peaches or pears, fruit compote (posh jam!) or a dollop of any red or yellow jam!

Fluffy Semolina or Sago

Add 1 or 2 eggs.

After simmering pudding in pan for 5 minutes and adding sugar, leave to cool for about 10 minutes. Separate whites and yolks, beat yolks well and whisk or stir into cool pudding mixture. Beat whites until stiff, fold into pudding and mix carefully. Bake in oven as above for 20 minutes and serve at once.

Crème Caramel

A useful pudding to make for a party, as it can be prepared the night before and left to set in the fridge until needed. Make a large caramel custard in a 1 litre/2 pint ovenproof soufflé dish or deep pie dish, or use dariole moulds or deep ramekin dishes for individual custards.

Serves 4

Preparation time: 15 minutes
Cooking time: Individual dishes ¾ to 1 hour
Large custard 1½ to 1¾ hours
Setting time: overnight in fridge

For Caramel:
75g/3 oz granulated sugar
3 tbsp water

For Custard:
4 eggs
50g/2 oz caster sugar
Few drops vanilla essence
600ml/1 pint milk – full cream if possible

Make caramel: Put granulated sugar and water into a heavy pan, and dissolve sugar over a low heat. Bring syrup to the boil and cook rapidly until syrup is a lovely golden brown. Carefully pour syrup into a large dish or 4-6 small dishes covering bases completely. Take care when handling hot caramel syrup.

Make custard: Heat oven at 150°C/300°F/fan oven 140°C/gas 2-3. Whisk together eggs, sugar and vanilla essence. Warm milk until just tepid (hand heat) and pour it into the egg mixture, whisking slowly. Butter sides of dishes above caramel, strain custard into each dish and place in a roasting tin half filled with hot water.

Bake in oven until a knife inserted in centre comes out clean. Remove from oven, leave to cool and refrigerate overnight.

Turn onto a serving dish or individual dishes and serve cold.

Egg Custard Tart

A family favourite when my children were young, known by them as 'Drinking Egg Pie', named after the special egg nog milk drink they all liked.

Serves 4   *Preparation & cooking time: 1 hour*

Rich Short Pastry:
175g/6 oz plain flour
75g/3 oz butter or margarine
1 egg
6-8 tsp cold water to mix

Custard:
2 eggs
1 tbsp granulated sugar
½ tsp vanilla essence
300ml/½ pint milk – full cream if possible
Little grated nutmeg or mixed spice

Heat oven at 200°C/400°F/fan oven 180°C/gas 6-7.

Make pastry in food processor or by hand – rub flour and fat together, separate egg, beat yolk with a little cold water and add to pastry mix, adding more water to make a stiff dough.

Roll out pastry and use to line an 18cm/7 inch deep flan tin.

Brush base and sides with the egg white, prick well with a fork, line case with a piece of cooking foil to hold it in shape and bake for 10 minutes, removing foil for last 2 or 3 minutes.

Lower oven heat to 170°C/325°F/fan oven 150°C/gas 3-4.

Make custard by whisking eggs, sugar and vanilla essence together well, and gradually beating in the milk. Pour custard into prepared pastry case, sprinkle with nutmeg or mixed spice.

Bake in the low oven for 30 to 40 minutes, until just firm but still a little soft, as the custard will set as it cools.

Allow to cool completely, remove flan ring and serve cold.

Queen's Pudding

A real, old, childhood favourite – how long since you saw this pudding on the menu? Why not make it for a special treat?

Serves 4   *Preparation & cooking time: 1½-2 hours including 30 minutes' standing time*

75g/3 oz fresh breadcrumbs – traditionally white bread
25g/1 oz granulated sugar
450ml/¾ pint milk
25g/1 oz butter or margarine
½ tsp vanilla essence and/or grated rind of 1 lemon
2 eggs
2-3 tbsp jam – traditionally raspberry
75g/3 oz caster sugar
Few glacé cherries and a little angelica for decoration

Mix breadcrumbs and sugar in a bowl or basin. Heat milk, butter, vanilla essence and/or lemon rind over a low heat until butter is melted. Pour over breadcrumb mix well and soak for 20-30 minutes until bread is swollen.

Heat oven at 170°C/325°F/fan oven 150°C/gas 3-4.

Well butter a 900ml/1½ pint pie dish. Separate eggs; beat yolks, stir into bread mixture and pour pudding into pie dish.

Bake in the low oven for 20-30 minutes until firm and just set. Warm chosen jam and spread carefully over pudding.

Make meringue: Whisk egg whites until stiff, then beat in caster sugar one teaspoon at a time. Pile meringue attractively on top of pudding, covering it completely.

Return pudding to oven and bake for a further 20-30 minutes, until meringue is firm and the peaks are pale golden brown. Decorate with glacé cherries and angelica. Serve hot or cold.

Chocolate Queen's Pudding

Add 25g/1 oz grated chocolate. Heat with milk, butter and vanilla essence, and omit grated lemon rind.

Magic Honeycomb Mould

Magic milk jelly – the layers separate as it sets!

Serves 4-6   Prep. & cooking time: 15 minutes + setting time

2 eggs
2 tbsp granulated sugar or runny honey
600ml/1 pint milk – preferably full cream
12g/½ oz or 1 envelope gelatine
2 tbsp hot water

Flavourings – choose one, they're all nice!
Grated rind and juice of 1 lemon or orange
1 tsp vanilla essence or 1-2 tsp strong black coffee

Separate eggs, put whites aside, and whisk together egg yolks, sugar or honey until pale and creamy.

Well rinse a heavy pan and warm milk slowly, with lemon or orange rind if used, until hot but not boiling. Whisk a little hot milk into the yolk mixture, then whisk this into the hot milk in the pan, and heat very gently until the mixture thickens, stirring or whisking all the time.

Strain custard into a large, clean saucepan and leave to cool.

Dissolve gelatine in a little hot water, and stir into the custard with the lemon or orange juice, vanilla essence or coffee.

Whisk egg whites until stiff but not brittle and fold thoroughly into the custard mixture.

Reheat custard over a gentle heat until hot but not boiling.

Rinse a 900ml/1½ pint deep mould or basin with cold water, pour in custard mixture, cool and leave in the fridge where it should separate as it sets.

When completely set, unmould carefully onto a serving dish – the creamy base will be topped by the flavoured jelly. Decorate with piped rosettes or swirls of cream, and serve with fresh strawberries or raspberries if liked.

Bread and Butter Pudding

The schoolday pudding that everyone remembers with either delight or disgust! It was the speciality of my daughter Annabel's cookery class, much to the delight of one of our neighbours who was always happy to eat it! However, this recipe makes such a delicious pud that I defy anyone not to enjoy it.

Serves 4-6
Prep. & cooking time: 1 hour + 30 minutes soaking

75g/3-4 oz butter, well softened
6-8 slices bread from a large loaf (white or brown)
100g/4 oz currants, sultanas, raisins or mixed dried fruit
75g/3 oz granulated sugar
2 eggs
450ml/¾ pint milk
½ tsp vanilla essence or grated rind of 1 lemon

Well butter a 900ml/1½ pint deep pie dish or ovenproof dish. Butter bread slices – I prefer to leave the crusts on for extra crunch. Cut into triangles and arrange half the slices in a layer on the base of the dish, butter side down.

Sprinkle with all the washed dried fruit, lemon rind if used and 1 heaped tablespoon sugar. Top with the rest of the bread, butter side up, and sprinkle with remaining sugar.

Beat eggs well, mix in the milk and vanilla essence if used, and pour over pudding, making sure all the bread is covered.

Leave to soak for at least 30 minutes until the bread has soaked up nearly all the milk – it can stand longer if needed.

Heat oven at 170°C/325°F/fan oven 150°C/gas 3-4.

Bake pudding in the moderate oven for 30-40 minutes until risen and set, with a lovely crispy golden top.

Serve hot with thick cream or crème fraîche.

Magic Islands

A special floating island pudding, named for Amy and Alicia who spend a lot of time on the magic Isle of Tiree.

Serves 4   Prep. & cooking time: 25 minutes + cooling time

Islands: **2 egg whites**
75g/3 oz caster sugar

Sea: **600ml/1 pint milk – full cream if possible**
2 eggs plus the 2 egg yolks left from the islands
50g/2 oz granulated sugar
1 tsp cornflour
½ tsp vanilla essence
Kitchen paper or cooking parchment for draining

A plainer custard ocean can be made using just the 2 egg yolks and 1 tbsp cornflour, instead of the two whole eggs and 1 tsp cornflour.

Make meringue islands: Whisk egg whites in a large bowl until thick, then gradually beat in sugar, 1 tsp at a time, to make a stiff meringue mix.

Pour milk into a large, very clean frying pan. Heat gently until hot but not boiling. Slide large spoonfuls of meringue onto milk and poach over a low heat for 4-5 minutes until set – allow 1 large or 2 small islands each. Carefully lift each island out with a fish slice or slotted spoon and leave to drain on kitchen paper. Remove milk from heat and keep aside.

Make custard sea: Whisk whole eggs, egg yolks, sugar, cornflour and vanilla essence together in a large bowl until pale and creamy, then slowly whisk in the warm milk from the pan.

Stand bowl over a large saucepan of hot water, or pour custard into top of a double boiler over hot water, and cook over a moderate heat stirring continuously until custard thickens.

Pour custard sea into a wide heatproof dish and float meringue islands on top. Leave to cool slightly but these islands are nicest served just warm, not chilled in the fridge.

Pancakes

Pancakes are one of the most versatile 'puddings', far too nice to be eaten only once a year on Shrove Tuesday or Pancake Day. They can be served straight from the pan with the traditional sugar and squeeze of lemon or made in advance, reheated and served with a wide variety of fillings and sauces.

Serves 4 – makes 8 to 10 pancakes

Preparation & cooking time: 15 minutes
+ 20 minutes' standing time if possible but not essential!

100g/4 oz plain flour
¼ tsp salt
1 egg
300ml/½ pint milk
oil or cooking fat for frying – an oil spray is ideal

Sieve flour and salt into a mixing bowl, add egg and beat well, using a wooden spoon or electric mixer. Gradually beat in milk to form a smooth batter, and pour into a jug. If time allows, leave to stand in fridge for 20 minutes.

Heat an omelette or small frying pan (18cm/7 in) over a moderate heat. When hot, lightly grease pan with a smear of oil or fat, pour in just enough batter to cover pan thinly, tilting pan to spread batter evenly. Fry briskly, for about half a minute, shaking pan a little to stop pancake sticking, until set on top and brown underneath. Toss or flip over with a knife and fry to cook the other side.

Turn pancake onto a warm plate, spread with chosen filling and eat at once, or keep warm covered with foil in a low oven. Wipe pan with kitchen paper, re-heat and re-grease pan, and cook the next pancake as before, until all the batter is used.

Pancakes can be left in the fridge overnight, stacked flat and covered with foil, or stacked, wrapped and frozen for later.

To reheat: Defrost if necessary, stack pancakes on an oven-proof plate, cover with foil and leave in a low oven, 150°F/ 300°C/fan oven 140°C/gas 2-3, until needed.

Traditional Lemon Pancakes

Sprinkle each pancake with caster sugar and a squeeze of lemon juice. Roll pancake, dredge with caster sugar and serve with a lemon wedge or Charlbury Lemon Sauce (page 122).

Syrup Pancakes

Use plain or flavoured maple or golden syrup. Pour a little over each pancake, fold into triangles (fold in half and half again). Serve with extra syrup or Sticky Syrup Sauce (page 122).

Crunchy Honey and Walnut Pancakes

Pour a little runny honey over each pancake, sprinkle with chopped nuts and roll or fold into triangles. Serve with a jug of warmed honey and a dollop of thickly whipped cream crème fraîche or vanilla ice cream if liked – scrummy!

Chocolate Pancakes

Sprinkle each pancake with 1-2 tsp drinking chocolate, top with a knob of unsalted butter, roll up and serve at once.

Jammy Pancakes – for those with a sweet tooth!

Spreading each pancake with a large spoonful of your favourite jam or fruit conserve is gorgeous! Roll or fold pancakes into triangles, dredge with caster sugar and serve at once with Jam Sauce if liked (page 122).

Fruity Pancakes

Use warmed cooked fruit (apple, blackberry, gooseberry, etc.), fresh soft fruit (strawberries, raspberries) or canned fruit slices. Spread chosen fruit over each pancake. Roll up, dredge with caster sugar, and serve at once with any extra juice or syrup.

Christmas Time Pancakes

Make filling: Peel, core and slice 225g/8 oz cooking apples and cook gently in a pan with 1-2 tbsp white wine or cider until soft. Mash with a fork, sweeten to taste with demerara sugar, stir in 1-2 tbsp mincemeat and a good pinch of cinnamon or mixed spice.

Spread filling over warm pancakes, fold into triangles, melt a knob of butter in frying pan over a moderate heat, add pancakes and reheat, turning carefully to warm both sides. Serve hot, with a bowl of brandy butter, whipped cream or crème fraîche.

Crêpes Suzette

Fun and easy to serve when you want to show off your dinner party skills – but have a practice run with the family first!

Serves 4

Pre-preparation time: 35 minutes to make and cook pancakes
Cooking & presentation time: 15 minutes

8 thin pancakes – prepared and stacked as on page 48
100g/4 oz unsalted butter
100g/4 oz caster sugar
Grated rind and juice of 2 oranges
3 tbsp Cointreau, Grand Marnier or Orange Curaçao
1-2 tbsp brandy for flaming

Prepare crêpes – spreading pancake batter really thinly across the pan to make them as thin as possible. Stack until needed.

Beat together butter, sugar and grated orange rind until soft and creamy, gradually adding 2-3 tbsp orange juice. Put aside, saving remaining juice. (The butter can be prepared in advance and frozen, defrosting before use.)

To serve: Heat a very clean, large (25cm/10 in) frying pan (or chafing-dish if you have one) over a moderate heat. Add the orange butter, reserved orange juice and chosen orange liqueur, heating gently until the butter is melted.

Slide the first crêpe into the pan, spoon the sauce over and allow to warm thoroughly. Fold crêpe in half and then in half again to make a triangle and move to the side of the pan. Add next crêpe and repeat until all crêpes are cooked and soaked in the lovely sauce, spooning remaining sauce over cooked crêpes.

Now for the fun bit! At the table, so that everyone can watch, pour the brandy into a warmed ladle and carefully set light to it (rather like flaming the Christmas Pudding!). Pour lighted brandy over crêpes, shaking pan to spread the flames. Serve crêpes at once, with the remaining sauce spooned over each plate.

4

CHOCOLATE HEAVEN

*Plain, milk or white chocolate
– it's paradise for chocoholics!*

Double Chocolate Biscuit Cake

A firm favourite with children and adults. Can be eaten as a dessert or a rich, teatime treat.

NB This cake contains raw egg and should not be served to very young children, pregnant women or elderly people.

Serves 4-6

Preparation time: 20 minutes   *Chilling time: overnight*

225g/8 oz chocolate chip or chocolate digestive biscuits
225g/8 oz plain cooking chocolate
225g/8 oz unsalted butter
2 eggs
½ tsp vanilla or almond essence
1 tbsp caster sugar
50g/2 oz grated chocolate (plain and/or milk) to decorate

Oil base and sides of an 18cm/7 in spring form tin or loose-based cake tin.

Roughly break biscuits into a bowl and break into crumbly pieces but not into crumbs (I pound them carefully with the end of a rolling pin).

Put chocolate into a heatproof basin and melt in a microwave or over a pan of simmering water. Keep warm until needed.

Melt butter gently in a small pan, then remove from heat.

Whisk eggs, essence and sugar in a basin until frothy, then beat in melted butter and mix well.

Pour melted chocolate into egg mixture, stir in the broken biscuits and mix gently to combine all the ingredients.

Spoon into prepared tin, smooth top of cake with a palette knife dipped in hot water and sprinkle with the grated chocolate. Refrigerate overnight.

To serve: Unclip spring form tin if used. Carefully push base of cake upwards and remove from tin. Using a clean fish slice loosen base of cake and slide it onto a serving plate.

The Chocolate Mousse

A very rich and always popular dessert. It can be flavoured with orange juice or rum, sherry, brandy, Cointreau etc., but we think it's gorgeous on its own with lovely thick cream.

NB This recipe contains raw egg and should not be given to very young children, pregnant women or elderly people.

Serves 4-6 depending on size of servings!

Preparation time: 20 minutes

175g/6 oz plain cooking chocolate
4 eggs
1 tsp vanilla essence
Juice of 1 orange – if liked
Small wine glass rum, sherry, brandy, Cointreau – if liked

Put chocolate into a large heatproof bowl and melt in a microwave or over a pan of simmering water.

Separate eggs. Put whites into a large bowl and whisk until stiff but not dry.

Put yolks and vanilla essence into a smaller basin and whisk until runny, adding orange juice or alcohol if used.

Remove melted chocolate from heat, and beat egg mixture into chocolate to make a smooth, shiny mixture.

Using a metal spoon, carefully fold beaten egg whites into chocolate mixture, taking care not to burst the air bubbles.

Pour into a large, glass serving dish, small glasses or sundae dishes. Or be trendy and serve in little coffee cups standing on tiny saucers.

Refrigerate until needed.

Serve with Mary's Chocolate Chip Cookies (see page 126), and a bowl of thick whipped cream.

Chocolate Filled Chocolate Roulade

A wickedly rich chocolate pudding – it's so popular with my family, especially Jon, who chose it as a wedding dessert, and even Mark, who prefers savouries, that I always make one at Christmas, stick a robin on top and call it the Chocolate Log.

Serves 8-10   *Preparation & cooking time: about 1 hour*

8 eggs, separated
225g/8 oz caster sugar
50g/2 oz (2 heaped tbsp) cocoa

Filling and Topping:
Fudgy Chocolate Filling, prepared in advance, see page 118
300ml/½ pint double cream, whipped stiffly

Heat oven at 180°C/350°F/fan oven 160°C/gas 4-5. Oil a large 33 × 21cm /13 × 9 in Swiss roll tin and line it with greaseproof paper or baking parchment, fitting paper to come 5cm/2 in above sides of the tin. Oil the paper or parchment.

Whip yolks and sugar in a large bowl until thick and creamy.

Sieve cocoa and fold into egg mixture.

Beat egg whites until stiff, but not hard, and fold carefully into creamy mixture, using a metal spoon.

Pour mixture into lined tin, gently spreading mixture evenly, and bake for 20-25 minutes, until well risen and springy to the touch. Do not overcook or it will break when rolled.

Take cake from oven, and leave to cool in tin (it will shrink a bit as it cools). Oil a sheet of greaseproof paper or baking parchment, sprinkle with caster sugar and turn cake onto it. Peel off lining paper and cut off any crispy cake edges.

When completely cold, spread cake with the prepared chocolate fudge filling and spread with whipped cream, saving some to decorate. Roll up carefully (the cake will crack a little as it is rolled), slide cake onto a serving dish and pipe whipped cream along the top for decoration.

Chocolate Profiterole Pyramid for Annabel

My favourite daughter's favourite childhood pudding! A showy dessert, often the centre piece in the window display of expensive patisseries. The little choux buns can be made in advance, but assemble the profiteroles just before serving.

Serves 6   *Preparation & cooking time: 45 minutes*
                              Assembly time: 10-15 minutes

Choux Buns:	**150ml/¼ pint water**
	50g/2 oz butter
	65g/2½ oz plain flour
	2 eggs, well beaten
Filling:	**300ml/½ pint double cream**
	½ tsp vanilla essence
	2 tsp caster sugar
Sauce:	**225g/8 oz plain cooking chocolate**
	2 tbsp water
	50g/2 oz butter

Heat oven at 200°C/400°F/fan oven 180°C/gas 6-7. Well grease 2 large baking trays.

Put water and butter in a pan, bring to the boil. Remove from heat, add all the flour at once, and beat with a wooden spoon to form a ball. Beat eggs in gradually to make a smooth paste. Using two spoons, drop round teaspoonfuls of paste onto the trays, spacing them well – makes 18-24 choux buns.

Bake in the hot oven for 25-30 minutes until buns are puffed and well risen, crisp and golden brown. Put onto a wire rack to cool, making a little slit in each bun to let out the steam.

Whip cream with vanilla essence and sugar until stiff.

Make chocolate sauce: Put all the ingredients in a bowl over a pan of simmering water. Stir until melted into a smooth sauce.

When ready to serve, split buns in half and fill with the cream. Arrange buns on a serving dish to form a wide pyramid, and pour or spoon the warm sauce over the top, to coat each bun.

Serve and enjoy at once.

Fudgy Chocolate Fondue

A fun dessert – omit the liqueur if children will be joining in, and take care that they do not touch the hot fondue pot. Use a heavy-based pot for this fondue to ensure the chocolate does not burn at the bottom of the bowl.

Serves 4-6   *Preparation time: 10 minutes*

500g/1 lb plain cooking chocolate
2 tbsp soft brown sugar
150ml/5 fl oz double cream
½ tsp vanilla essence
2-3 tbsp brandy, rum or Tia Maria
To Dip: strawberries, banana slices, dessert apple slices,
    Kiwi fruit (peeled and chunked), seedless grapes
    pineapple chunks, peach slices (fresh or canned)
    dried sweetened fruit (sold in pre-packed cartons)
    marshmallows, tiny macaroons

Break chocolate into pieces and put into a basin with the sugar over a pan of simmering water, and allow to melt, stirring occasionally with a wooden spoon until mixed. Stir in cream, vanilla essence and brandy, rum or Tia Maria if used, and beat gently to make a rich, smooth sauce.

Prepare chosen fruits, marshmallows or macaroons, and place in dishes on the table, or make up a small mixed dish for each person and put with their fondue fork.

Pour warm chocolate mix into the fondue pot, carry to the table and place over the lighted burner – do not allow the fondue to get too hot and boil or burn.

White Chocolate Fondue

Use white cooking chocolate and caster sugar, and substitute a cream liqueur for the brandy, rum or Tia Maria.

If you are entertaining a larger number of people, use two fondue pots (borrow one from one of the guests if necessary), and make a dark and a white fondue – lovely!

Alexandrena's Tipsy Wedding Cake

For her son's wedding, my friend covered this chocolate cake with white fondant icing to match the traditional fruit cake tiers, making a perfect wedding cake for 'those who don't like rich fruit cake!' For a super pudding, cover the tipsy cake in a swirl of tipsy fudge topping and serve with a bowl of tipsy cream!

Serves 6-8   Prep. & cooking time: 1 hour + cooling and icing

175g/6 oz plain cooking chocolate
75g/3 oz soft pale brown sugar
100g/4 oz butter
3 eggs, separated
½ tsp almond essence
100g/4 oz ground almonds
1 tbsp drinking chocolate dissolved in 4 tbsp hot water
3-4 tbsp brandy, whisky or rum according to taste
50g/2 oz plain flour, sieved

Topping: **175g/6 oz plain cooking chocolate**
              1-2 tbsp brandy, whisky or rum as in the cake
              50g/2 oz butter

To serve: **300ml/½ pint double cream, whipped**
              1-2 tsp brandy, whisky or rum as in the cake

Heat oven at 180°C/350°F/fan oven 160°C/gas 4-5. Grease a 20cm/8 in cake tin, and line base with greaseproof paper. Melt chocolate in a bowl over simmering water.

Cream sugar and butter until fluffy and creamy. Whisk yolks and essence until creamy and gradually beat into mixture. Stir in ground almonds. Mix drinking chocolate and alcohol into melted chocolate and stir into cake mix with the flour.

Beat egg whites until very stiff, and fold carefully into cake. Spoon into tin, and bake for 25-35 minutes, until risen and springy to the touch. Cool slightly, then turn onto wire rack.

Make topping: Melt chocolate, stir in alcohol and butter and beat until smooth and shiny. Leave in fridge until set enough to swirl over the cold cake with a palette knife. Serve with whipped cream flavoured with brandy, whisky or rum, or plain pouring cream if preferred.

Baked Chocolate Soufflé

A hot soufflé is much easier to make than one is sometimes led to believe, and looks impressive served straight from the oven (soufflés don't wait), risen well above the rim of the dish. Make one large soufflé or individual ones, they're both nice.

Serves 4

Preparation: 20 minutes   *Cooking time: 40 minutes large*
                                               20 minutes small

100g/4 oz plain cooking chocolate
1 tbsp water
50g/2 oz butter
50g/2 oz plain flour
300ml/½ pint milk
½ tsp vanilla essence
4 eggs, separated
50g/2 oz caster sugar
Icing sugar to decorate

Heat oven at 190°C/375°F/fan oven 170°C/gas 5-6. Well grease a 1 litre/2 pint soufflé dish or 4 individual dishes.

Put chocolate and water in a basin and melt gently in a microwave or over a pan of simmering water.

Melt butter in a small pan, stir in flour and cook until it forms a ball, beating well. Remove from heat, gradually stir in milk, return to heat and cook, stirring hard, until sauce thickens. Beat in melted chocolate and vanilla essence and put to cool.

Beat egg yolks, and beat into soufflé mixture a little at a time. Whisk egg whites until stiff, then whisk in sugar a teaspoon at a time until stiff but not hard, and fold carefully into soufflé.

Pour into prepared dish or dishes and bake in the hot oven, times as above, until well risen and top is firm.

Remove from oven, dust top with icing sugar and serve at once to accompanying 'oohs and ahs' of admiration! The soufflé is even better served with thick pouring cream.

Mississippi Mud Pie

My American daughter-in-law tells me this is just for the tourists, but it tastes good whoever's eating it! Omit liqueur if serving the pie to children.

Serves 6-8   Preparation time: 20 minutes + freezing time

175g/6 oz digestive biscuits, plain or chocolate
175g/6 oz plain cooking chocolate
50g/2 oz unsalted butter
1 tbsp caster sugar
600ml/1 pint chocolate chip or chocolate ice cream
600ml/1 pint coffee ice cream
3-4 tbsp Irish Coffee Cream liqueur or brandy

To decorate:
2-3 tbsp grated chocolate
300ml/½ pint whipped cream – flavoured with 2-3 tsp
 liqueur, as in pie, if liked

Grease a 20-23cm/8-9 in freezerproof flan dish.

Crush biscuits into crumbs (put into a bowl or strong polythene bag and crush gently with a rolling pin).

Put chocolate in a large bowl and melt in a microwave or over a pan of simmering water. Remove from heat.

Beat butter into chocolate, stir in sugar and biscuit crumbs and press over base and sides of flan dish. Chill in fridge.

Mix ice creams in a bowl, add liqueur if used, and beat with a wooden spoon to soften a little and blend together.

Spoon filling on top of cold flan case and smooth top. Freeze until needed.

To serve: Take pie from freezer and leave to soften but not melt, in the fridge or kitchen, for 15-30 minutes according to temperature.

Sprinkle with grated chocolate, and serve with whipped cream.

Chocolate Almond Charlotte

A 'proper' party dessert! The whisky is optional, as it tastes really delicious either teetotal or alcoholic!

Serves 8-10 – it's very rich   *Preparation time: 20 minutes +*
chilling and setting time

1 packet sponge finger biscuits
175g/6 oz plain cooking chocolate
175g/6 oz butter plus a little extra for fixing sponge fingers
75g/3 oz soft pale brown sugar
½ tsp almond essence
100g/4 oz ground almonds
2 tbsp whisky – optional
300ml/½ pint double cream

To decorate:
Piped whipped cream or aerosol cream
50g/2 oz finely chopped nuts
Length of narrow ribbon to tie round dessert

Well oil a 20cm/8 in loose-based cake tin or Charlotte mould, and line base with oiled greaseproof paper. Line sides of cake tin or mould with sponge biscuits – smear edges of biscuits with butter to help them stick together.

Put chocolate into a basin and melt in microwave or over a pan of simmering water.

Whisk butter and sugar and almond essence together until fluffy and light, beat in ground almonds, and stir in chocolate. Beat in whisky (if used) a little at a time.

Whip cream until thick but not solid and fold gently into the chocolate mixture. Pour into prepared tin or mould and chill in fridge for several hours until completely set.

To serve: Turn out very carefully onto serving plate, and remove paper. Decorate with cream rosettes or swirls, and sprinkle with the chopped nuts. Tie a narrow ribbon around the centre of the sponge biscuits and take to the table at once.

Triple Chocolate Meringue Flan

A rich chocolate filling on a crisp chocolate biscuit crust, topped with sprinkled chocolate meringue.

Serves 6   *Preparation & cooking time: about 1 hour*

Flan case:	**225g/8 oz plain chocolate digestive biscuits**
	100g/4 oz butter
Filling:	**100g/4 oz soft pale brown sugar**
	3 tbsp cornflour
	3 egg yolks – whisked until runny
	300ml/½ pint milk
	100g/4 oz plain cooking chocolate
	25g/1 oz butter
Topping:	**3 egg whites**
	100g/4 oz caster sugar
	2 tbsp sweetened drinking chocolate
	2/3 tsp grated chocoate

Heat oven at 150°C/300°F/fan oven 140°C/gas 2-3.

Make flan case: Put biscuits in a bowl or plastic bag and crush into large crumbs. Melt butter, stir in biscuit crumbs and press over base and sides of a 20-22cm/8-9 in flan dish.

Make filling: Put sugar, cornflour and well whisked egg yolks into a bowl, and whisk together until smooth. Heat milk and chocolate in a pan over a low heat until chocolate is melted, then pour gradually over filling mixture, whisking to make a smooth sauce. Pour sauce back into pan and whisk over a low heat until sauce thickens. Whisk in butter making a rich, chocolatey filling, cool for a few minutes and then pour into the flan case.

Make meringue: Whisk egg whites until thick, then whisk in sugar 1 tsp at a time until meringue is stiff and creamy.

Slowly whisk or fold in drinking chocolate (if you whisk fast the powder blows everywhere!), and pile meringue over flan.

Bake in the low oven for 20 minutes until meringue is crisp. Leave flan to cool, then sprinkle with grated chocolate and serve with thickly whipped chocolate cream – see page 117.

Cold Mocha Soufflé

A light, delicious dessert which looks impressive and tastes wonderful.

NB This recipe contains raw egg and should not be given to young children, pregnant women or elderly people.

Serves 4-6   Preparation time: 30-40 minutes + setting time

4 eggs – separated
75g/3 oz caster sugar
175g/6 oz plain cooking chocolate
1-2 tbsp instant coffee granules
12g/1 envelope gelatine
150ml/¼ pint double cream

To decorate: **150ml/¼ pint double cream**
                  1-2 tsp ready made strong coffee
                  2-3 tbsp grated chocolate

Prepare an 18cm/7 in soufflé dish as for Saint Clement's Soufflé – see page 75.

Put egg yolks and sugar into a heatproof bowl over a pan of simmering water and whisk until creamy and thick enough to leave a trail when shaken from the whisk. Remove from heat and leave to cool.

Put chocolate into another bowl and put to melt over the simmering water.

Put instant coffee and gelatine in a little bowl or cup, mix in 6 tbsp boiling water and stir until both have dissolved.

Remove melted chocolate from the heat, stir in coffee and gelatine, cool slightly and then fold it all into the egg mixture.

Whisk cream until thick but not solid and fold into the soufflé and finally whip egg whites until stiff and fold in gently. Pour soufflé into the prepared dish and chill until needed.

To serve: Carefully remove collar – see page 75. Whip cream with coffee until stiff, and pipe around soufflé. Sprinkle top with grated chocolate and keep cool until served.

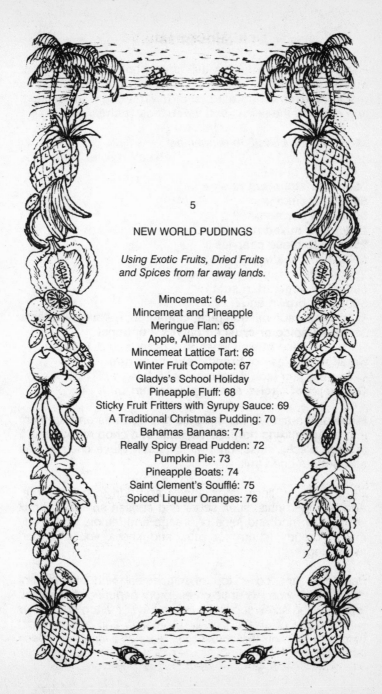

5

NEW WORLD PUDDINGS

*Using Exotic Fruits, Dried Fruits
and Spices from far away lands.*

Mincemeat

Homemade mincemeat is the most wonderful melange of fruit and spices from far away lands. It's quick and easy to make, requires no cooking, and, unlike bought mincemeat, you can add the spices and flavourings you really like.

Makes about 4.5kg/8 lb mincemeat
Preparation time: 30 minutes

500g/1 lb stoneless raisins
500g/1 lb sultanas
500g/1 lb currants
250g/½ lb mixed peel
250g/½ lb glacé cherries
500g/1 lb cooking apples
250g/½ lb chopped mixed nuts
500g/1 lb vegetarian suet
500g/soft brown sugar
½ to 1 tsp each mixed spice, cinnamon, nutmeg – to taste
¼ tsp all spice or crushed cloves – optional
Rind and juice of well washed 1 orange and 1 lemon
Small wine glass of brandy, sherry or rum
Clean dry jam jars, preferably with lids
Greaseproof circles and/or plastic film

Rinse and drain raisins, sultanas and currants and tip them into a large mixing bowl. Rinse, drain and chop mixed peel, if in large pieces, rinse, drain and quarter glacé cherries and add both to dried fruit.

Peel, core and finely chop apples and add to fruit mixture. Add chopped nuts, suet, sugar and chosen spices and mix well. Stir in rind and juice of orange and lemon, and finally mix in brandy, sherry or rum, and check you've added everything!

Pack into jars, cover top of mincemeat with greaseproof circles. Screw on lids or tie greaseproof paper tightly over the tops. If using screw top lids, I like to cover the top of each jar with a piece of plastic film for protection and a better seal before putting on the screw top. Store in a dry, cool place until needed.

Mincemeat and Pineapple Meringue Flan

A real winter treat, especially if filled with homemade mincemeat. The filled flan can be frozen until needed, then defrosted and covered with meringue topping before serving.

Serves 6-8
> *Preparation & cooking time: 1 hour + cooling time*

Rich short pastry: **175g/6 oz plain flour with pinch of salt**
75g/3 oz butter or margarine
2 egg yolks
6-8 tsp cold water to mix

Filling: **425g can pineapple pieces in juice**
225g/8 oz mincemeat

Meringue: **2 egg whites**
100g/4 oz caster sugar

To decorate: **Few glacé cherries and angelica**

Heat oven at 200°C/400°F/fan oven 180°C/gas 6-7. Make pastry in food processor or by hand – rub flour and fat together, beat egg yolks with a little cold water and mix into pastry, adding enough cold water to make a stiff dough.

Roll out pastry and use to line a 20cm/8 in flan dish or ring. Line case with a piece of cooking foil to hold it in shape, and bake for 10 minutes, removing foil for last 2 or 3 minutes.

Take pastry case from oven, remove flan ring if used, and leave to cool. Lower oven heat to 150°C/300°F/fan oven 140°C/gas 2-3.

Drain pineapple, reserving the juice. Cover base of flan with half the mincemeat, spoon in the pineapple and top with the remaining mincemeat.

Make meringue: Beat egg whites until stiff, then beat in sugar a teaspoon at a time. Pile meringue prettily over top of flan.

Bake in the cool oven for 20-30 minutes until meringue is firm and crisp and the peaks are a pale golden brown.

Decorate with glacé cherries and angelica. Serve with thickly whipped cream, flavoured with a little pineapple juice if liked.

Apple, Almond and Mincemeat Lattice Tart

A quick and easy alternative to mince pies, but nice any time of the year.

Serves 6-8   *Preparation & cooking time: 1 hour*

**225g/8 oz shortcrust pastry – homemade see page 90
  or 340g pack bought pastry**

Filling: **225g/8 oz mincemeat
          500g/1 lb sweet dessert apples
          3 tbsp apricot jam
          2-3 tbsp cider or apple juice
          50g/2 oz flaked almonds
          Milk or beaten egg to glaze**

Heat oven at 200°C/400°F/fan oven 180°C/gas 6-7. Prepare homemade pastry (if used) as on page 90.

Roll out pastry and use to line base and sides of a 23cm/9 in round pie dish, pressing pastry into shape of dish. Trim edges and reserve the pastry trimmings.

Cover pastry base with mincemeat.

Peel and core apples, slice thinly, and arrange on top of the mincemeat.

Put apricot jam in a small pan with cider or apple juice and heat very gently until jam is melted.

Stir almonds into apricot sauce and pour over top of apples, making sure all the apples are coated with nuts and sauce.

Roll out pastry trimmings, cut into 1cm/½ in strips, and twist strips over top of flan to form a lattice topping, dampening ends with milk or beaten egg to hold in place.

Brush flan top and pastry lattice with milk or egg, and bake in the hot oven for 25-30 minutes until pastry is golden brown.

Serve warm with Almond Chantilly Crème, see page 124, thickly whipped double cream or crème fraîche.

Winter Fruit Compote

An up-to-date version of an old-fashioned favourite, and these days you can serve it in any season as you like. Today there are lots of dried fruits available all year round, both the traditional ones that need soaking and the newer, pre-prepared kinds. Some fresh winter fruits (oranges, mandarins, tangarines, grapes) can be added for extra colour and flavour. Choose a good mixture of fruits, varying flavours, colour and textures according to taste and availability.

Serves 4-6   *Preparation & cooking time: 25 minutes*
                                              + overnight soaking the night before

50g/2 oz dried apple rings
50g/2 oz dried apricots
50g/2 oz dried pears
50g/2 oz dried peaches
25g/1 oz prunes
100g/4 oz sweetened tropical mixed fruit
1 sweet dessert orange and/or mandarin
Small bunch seedless green and/or black grapes
Water to soak fruit
75g/3 oz granulated sugar
Thinly peeled rind of 1 lemon and/or orange
1 large wine glass pale sherry or white wine – optional

Put chosen dried fruit in a bowl, cover with water and soak overnight in the fridge.

Next day, drain fruit, pouring 300ml/½ pint of soaking water into a large pan with sugar and peeled rind. Bring to the boil and cook briskly for 5-6 minutes to make a thin syrup. Reduce heat to a simmer, add drained fruit and sherry or white wine if used, and simmer very gently for 10 minutes.

Remove pan from heat, mix in sweetened tropical fruit, orange or mandarin segments and washed grapes, taking care not to break up the fruit pieces.

Spoon into a deep glass serving dish and pour syrup over fruit. Serve warm or chilled, on its own or with pouring cream or custard. It is also a lovely served together with crème caramel.

Gladys's School Holiday Pineapple Fluff

Gladys gave me this recipe years ago when I needed a quick dessert for unexpected guests. An easy pudding, lovely for children as it looks and tastes special although it's not too rich. A great way to occupy them on a 'day with nothing to do'. Older ones can make it themselves (with a little supervision), and younger ones can help or hinder as they wish!

Serves 4

Preparation time: 30-60 minutes (jelly setting time will vary!)

1 packet (135g) pineapple or lemon jelly
1 large tin (425g) pineapple pieces or crushed pineapple, in syrup or fruit juice according to taste
1 small tin (225g) evaporated milk, chilled in the fridge
Aerosol cream for decoration – optional

Make jelly: Put jelly cubes into a heatproof measuring jug, add 150ml/5 fl oz boiling water and stir until dissolved.

Drain pineapple syrup or juice and stir it into jelly, then make mixture up to 600ml/1 pint with ice cubes or very cold water.

Stir jelly until ice cubes have melted, then put into fridge or freezer until jelly is still soft but is just beginning to set.

Whip evaporated milk in a large bowl until frothy and thick enough to write your initial on the cream before it sinks.

When jelly is just setting and ready, put aside a little of the pineapple for decoration and mix the rest into the jelly.

Then stir jelly mixture into the thickly whipped evaporated milk and whisk gently to mix.

Pour into a large serving dish or individual dishes and refrigerate until set.

Decorate with reserved pineapple and swirls of cream and serve at once.

Sticky Fruit Fritters with Syrupy Sauce

Delicious fruit in a light crispy batter, served dredged in sugar with the lovely sweet sauce. When cooked, the fritters need to be served as soon as possible.

Serves 4　　　　*Preparation & cooking time: 30-40 minutes*

100g/4 oz plain flour with a pinch of salt
1 tbsp vegetable oil
150m/¼ pint tepid water

Allow 3 fritters for each person using a mixture of fruit:
1 small fresh pineapple, peeled, cut into rings and cored
   or 425g can of pineapple rings
3 sweet dessert apples – peeled, cored and cut into rings
3 peaches – peeled, stoned and cut into slices
3 firm bananas – peeled, cut lengthways and then across

2 egg whites
Fat for deep frying
3 tbsp caster sugar mixed with 2 tsp cinnamon to dredge
Sticky Syrup Sauce to serve – see page 122

Make batter: Sieve flour and salt into bowl, mix in oil and enough tepid water to make a smooth paste, then beat well, using an electric mixer or wooden spoon. Put aside in the fridge.

Prepare the chosen fruit, drain well and dry on kitchen paper.

Whisk egg whites until stiff and fold into the batter.

Heat deep fat to 190°C/375°F – do not let fat get too hot. Dip pieces of prepared fruit into the batter (use cooking tongs), coat thoroughly and drain excess batter back into the bowl, only coating a few pieces at a time. Put into frying basket (do not over fill), lower basket into hot fat and fry fritters until golden, turning carefully to cook both sides.

Drain fritters on kitchen paper, dredge with cinnamon sugar, and keep hot until all the fritters are cooked.

Serve at once with a jug of warm Sticky Syrup Sauce.

A Traditional Christmas Pudding

A really rich, delicious pudding, stuffed with fruit and spices. Called 'Fire Pudding' by my granddaughters, Jillian and Joanne, who are entranced by the traditional pudding flaming ritual!

Makes one 1kg/2 lb pudding or two 500g/1 lb puddings

Serves 12   *Preparation time: 30 minutes*
Cooking time: 8 hours large pudding; 5-6 hours smaller puds

175g/6oz raisins, stoned and chopped, or stoneless
100g/4 oz each sultanas and currants
50g/2 oz cut mixed peel
100g/4 oz glacé cherries, rinsed and quartered
100g/4 oz chopped mixed nuts
1 medium cooking apple, peeled, cored and finely chopped
1 medium-sized carrot, peeled and finely grated
75g/3 oz self-raising flour
75g/3 oz fresh white breadcrumbs (or brown if preferred)
100g/4 oz shredded vegetarian suet
225g/8 oz soft brown sugar
1 tsp mixed spice
½ tsp each cinnamon and nutmeg
2 eggs – well beaten
Grated rind and juice of 1 orange and 1 lemon
3-4 tbsp beer, cider, stout or milk to mix
1 tbsp black treacle

Well grease a 1.2 litre/2 lb pudding basin or two 600ml/1 lb basins. Put fruit, dry ingredients and spices into mixing bowl. Add eggs, orange and lemon rind and juice, chosen liquid and treacle. Mix well, letting everyone have a stir and a wish.

Put into basin(s), cover with greased greaseproof paper and basin lid if it has one, and wrap basin loosely in foil. Boil or steam for appropriate time – see page 30.

Remove from pan, cool, and replace tops with fresh paper and foil. Store in a cool, dry place until needed.

On Christmas Day, boil or steam pud as before for 1-2 hours. Turn onto serving dish, top with holly and flame with brandy. Serve with Brandy Butter and/or Chantilly Crème (see page 124).

Bahamas Bananas

A quickly made but rather special dessert.

Serves 4
Preparation time: 5 minutes
Cooking time: 5 minutes – serve straight from the pan

4 large Bahamas Bananas, not too ripe
50g/2 oz unsalted butter
Juice of 1 sweet orange
1 tsp cinnamon
2-3 tbsp rum

To serve:
Pale gold muscavado sugar
Thick pouring cream

Peel bananas and slice in half lengthways.

Heat butter in a heavy, very clean frying pan, or chafing-dish if you have one, over a medium heat. Add sliced bananas, cut side down, and fry for a few minutes until pale and golden.

Turn bananas over carefully so that they do not break, pour the orange juice over the top and sprinkle with cinnamon. Fry for a few more minutes to brown the other side.

Take pan to the table, put rum into a warm ladle, set light to it carefully and pour over the bananas, shaking pan gently to spread the flames.

Use a long handled slice to dish the flaming bananas onto warmed plates and spoon some sauce over each helping.

Serve with a bowl of muscavado sugar and a jug of thick pouring cream.

Really Spicy Bread Pudden

A delicious way to use up stale bread. The pudden can be eaten hot as a dessert, or is perfect for a picnic cake or packed lunch when cold.

Serves 4-6

Preparation & cooking time: 1 hour + 30 minutes' soaking

225g/8 oz brown or white bread – granary is lovely
300ml/½ pint milk
175g/6 oz mixed dried fruit – bought as a mixture or mix
  your own raisins, sultanas, currants and peel
Grated rind and juice of 1 or 2 sweet oranges
100g/4 oz soft brown sugar
2-3 tsp mixed spice
1 tsp cinnamon
50g/2 oz butter – nicer than margarine if available
1 egg
Grated nutmeg

Break bread into small pieces in a mixing bowl, stir in milk, mix well and leave to soak in the fridge for about 30 minutes.

Put dried fruit into a basin, add orange rind and stir in orange juice. Leave to soak until bread mixture is ready

Heat oven at 180°C/350°F/fan oven 160°C/gas 4-5.

Well butter a 1.5 litre/2½ pint shallow ovenproof dish.

Take bread from fridge and stir in drained dried fruit (saving the orange juice), sugar, mixed spice, cinnamon and butter (melted, grated or chopped into tiny pieces).

Beat egg with reserved orange juice and pour into pudding mixture, stirring well. Spoon into prepared baking dish and sprinkle generously with freshly ground nutmeg.

Bake in the moderate oven for 50-60 minutes until set.

Serve hot with custard or cream if liked, or cold at teatime.

Pumpkin Pie

Not only for American Thanksgiving, it's good on any day.

Serves 6-8
Preparation & cooking time: 1-1½ hours approximately

**225g/8 oz shortcrust pastry (homemade, see page 90) or
340g pack bought pastry**

Filling:
1 large 450g can pumpkin purée
½ tsp salt
2 tsp cinnamon
1 tsp mixed spice
½ tsp each ground ginger and nutmeg
225g/8 oz pale brown sugar
2 eggs
300ml/½ pint double cream

Heat oven at 180°C/350°F/fan oven 160°C/gas 4-5. Make homemade pastry, if used, as on page 90.

Roll out pastry and use to line a 22cm/9 in deep pie dish, pressing pastry into shape of dish.

Trim edges, prick pastry base with a fork, and chill in fridge until needed.

Put pumpkin, salt and spices into a bowl and mix well.

Stir in sugar, well beaten eggs and cream.

Take pastry case from fridge and pour in pumpkin mixture.

Bake in the moderate oven for 45-50 minutes or until set. If pastry edges start to get too brown, cover top of pie loosely with a piece of foil until filling is cooked.

Serve hot or cold with a bowl of whipped cream or crème fraîche.

Pumpkin pie freezes well, and so can be made in advance and frozen, ready to defrost and reheat when needed.

Pineapple Boats

A pretty fruit salad served in the pineapple shells – a really showy dinner party dessert!

Serves 4 (but just buy more pineapples and increase the amount of fruit salad for extra guests)

Preparation time: 20 minutes

2 small pineapples with leaves on, ripe but not too soft
1 ripe comice pear
1 sweet red dessert apple
1 ripe Kiwi fruit
Small bunch seedless green grapes – about 75g/3 oz
Small bunch seedless black grapes – about 75g/3 oz
Little caster sugar to taste
1-2 tbsp fresh orange juice, white wine or Cointreau
Whipped cream to serve

Well rinse pineapples and cut in half lengthways, cutting through the leaves and leaving them attached to the fruit.

Carefully scoop out pineapple flesh, saving the shells. Remove cores, cut fruit into small, bite-sized pieces and put into a bowl.

Wash and core pear and apple (peel if you prefer but the skins add colour to the salad), cut into pieces and put into the bowl.

Peel Kiwi fruit, slice or cube and add to the other fruits.

Rinse grapes well, add to the fruit salad and mix gently.

Sprinkle with a little caster sugar to taste – if the pineapple is nice and sweet you may not need any sugar – and pour over the orange juice, white wine or Cointreau, stirring carefully to mix with the fruit. Cover with plastic film and chill until needed.

When ready, pile fruit into the pineapple shells, arrange on a serving dish and spoon any remaining syrup over the top. Serve at once with a bowl of whipped cream, which can be flavoured with 1-2 tsp orange juice, white wine or Cointreau if liked.

Saint Clement's Soufflé

For a really tangy fruit flavour, add grapefruit juice to the orange and lemon. **NB** This contains raw eggs and should not be given to young children, pregnant women or the elderly.

Serves 4   *Preparation time: 40 minutes + setting time*

3 eggs, separated
175g/6 oz caster sugar
Juice and rind of 1 orange, 1 lemon and 1 grapefruit
12g/½ oz envelope gelatine
300ml/½ pint whipping or double cream
1-2 tbsp Cointreau – if liked
To decorate: **Small, 225g can mandarin oranges**
                150g/¼ pint whipped double cream or
                aerosol cream

Using a 15cm/6 in soufflé dish, cut a collar of foil or double greaseproof paper long enough to go round the dish, overlapping by 5cm/2 in, and standing 8cm/3 in above the rim. Tie paper securely around dish, and lightly brush inside the dish and the top of the paper with vegetable oil.

Put egg yolks, sugar and fruit juices (save grated rinds) into a heatproof bowl over a pan of simmering water, and whisk until creamy and thick enough to leave a trail when shaken from the whisk. Remove from heat and allow to cool.

Tip gelatine in a small basin, add 3 tbsp boiling water, stir until completely dissolved and then stir into yolk mixture. Put mixture in fridge and leave until just beginning to set.

In separate bowls, beat egg whites until stiff, and whip cream, with Cointreau if used, until thick but not solid. When yolk mixture is ready, fold in cream and egg whites. Spoon into prepared dish, smooth top and chill until set.

To serve: Dip a palette knife in hot water and use to remove foil or paper collar, disturbing the soufflé as little as possible.

Sprinkle top of soufflé with the reserved rind. Arrange well drained mandarin oranges around edge of soufflé and decorate with piped rosettes or swirls of cream if liked.

Spiced Liqueur Oranges

An easily prepared dessert, great for a dinner party as it is best prepared the day before and left to chill overnight to absorb the lovely flavours.

Serves 6 – or allow 1 orange and 25g/1 oz sugar per person

Preparation time: 20 minutes   *Chilling time: 12-24 hours*

6 sweet, preferably seedless, dessert oranges
175g/6 oz caster or granulated sugar
150ml/¼ pint fresh orange juice
3 or 4 cloves
2-3 tbsp Grand Marnier, or any orange liqueur

Wash one orange well, and peel rind thinly, taking just the coloured part of the rind, and cut it into thin strips.

Put strips into a small pan, cover with water and bring to the boil. Remove from heat and leave to cool. Drain and reserve.

Put sugar, orange juice and cloves into a pan, heat until sugar is dissolved, then boil for 2-3 minutes to make a thin syrup.

Remove pan from heat, allow to cool and remove cloves.

Peel remaining oranges, removing all pith, and cut across into neat slices, discarding any pips.

Arrange orange slices attractively in a deep serving dish, add liqueur to the cool syrup and pour over oranges, making sure they are all drenched with some of the syrup.

Cover with plastic film and leave overnight in fridge.

When ready to serve, scatter with reserved orange strips.

Serve with thick cream.

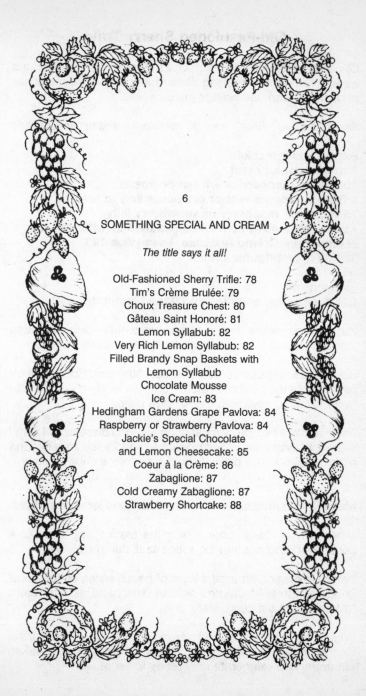

6

SOMETHING SPECIAL AND CREAM

The title says it all!

Old-Fashioned Sherry Trifle

Once the epitome of a high-class Sunday Tea, but now a wonderful memory-evoking dinner party dessert. If preferred, omit sherry and use orange juice instead.

Serves 6-8+   *Prep. time: 30 minutes + setting and chilling*

6 trifle sponge cakes
6 tbsp raspberry jam
100g/4 oz raspberries – fresh or frozen
6 tbsp sherry – sweet or dry according to taste
135g packet raspberry or strawberry jelly
About half a 454g can sliced peaches in juice or syrup
600ml/1 pint Crème Anglaise – see page 123
300ml/½ pint double cream

To decorate:
Glacé cherries, angelica and flaked almonds

Put sponge cakes into a large, glass trifle dish, breaking pieces to cover the base completely, and spread with jam.

Spread the raspberries over the top of the jam. Spoon sherry over raspberries, mix in gently, and leave sherry and raspberry juices to soak into the sponge cake.

Put jelly into a heatproof measuring jug, and dissolve in 150ml/¼ pint boiling water. Drain peaches, add juice to jelly, and make up to 600ml/1 pint with cold water or ice cubes. Leave in fridge or freezer until just beginning to set but still runny.

Make Crème Anglaise – see page 123 – and leave to go cold.

When jelly is ready, pour it over the raspberries to make a thick layer, and put into the fridge until completely set.

When jelly is set, arrange a layer of peach slices on top, pour or spoon the cold Crème Anglaise over peaches and return to fridge until set completely.

Whip cream until stiff, and spread thickly over top of trifle. Decorate with halved glacé cherries, angelica and flaked almonds, and refrigerate until ready to serve.

Tim's Crème Brulée

Very rich and absolutely gorgeous – my eldest son's favourite dessert. Make the crème the day before eating to give it time to set completely. The brulée only takes a few minutes but must be made no more than two or three hours before serving as it will not stay crisp. Serve this dessert really cold to enjoy the lovely creamy flavour.

Serves 4-6, depending on the size of the ramekin dishes
Preparation & cooking time: crème – 30 minutes
brulée – 5 minutes

Crème: **4 eggs**
2 heaped tbsp caster sugar
600ml/1 pint whipping cream
½ tsp vanilla essence

Brulée: **4-6 tbsp demerara sugar**
A few raspberries or strawberries to decorate
2 tsp caster sugar, to taste

Heat oven at 150°C/300°F/fan oven 140°C/gas 2-3.

Make crème: Put eggs and sugar into a bowl or mixer and whisk together gently, then mix in cream and vanilla essence. Pour into ramekin dishes, filling to about 1cm/½ in from the top.

Stand ramekins in a clean, roasting tin or large ovenproof dish and pour 3cm/1 in hot water into the dish, enough to come just halfway up the ramekins. Bake for 15-20 minutes until nearly set – do not overcook, as the crème will set as it cools.

Allow to cool, and leave overnight in the fridge.

Make brulée: 2-3 hours before serving, heat grill until very hot.

Cover top of each crème with a layer of demerara sugar, place on grill pan and brown for 1-2 minutes until sugar has melted and turned crispy, or melt sugar with a chef's blow torch. Allow to cool and chill in fridge until ready to serve.

Serve plain or decorated with a few fresh raspberries or sliced strawberries, tossed in caster sugar if liked.

Choux Treasure Chest

Fill the treasure chest with fabulous jewels and gold pieces by using fresh berries, grapes, mixed fruit or golden peach slices.

Serves 4-6   *Preparation & cooking time: 1-1¼ hours*

Choux Pastry: **150ml/¼ pint water**
                    50g/2 oz butter
                    65g/2½ oz plain flour
                    2 eggs – well beaten

Filling: **300ml/½ pint double cream**
                    500g/1 lb fresh or canned fruit to taste –
                    fresh strawberries, raspberries or
                    seedless grapes canned peach slices,
                    fruit cocktail or cherries
                    1-2 tbsp icing sugar to taste

Heat oven at 200°C/400°F/ fan oven 180°C/ gas 6-7. Put water and butter in a pan, bring to the boil. Remove from heat, add all the flour at once and beat with a wooden spoon to form a ball. Beat eggs in gradually to make a smooth paste.

Use two tablespoons to form paste into a long, smooth strip, 25 × 5cm/10 × 2 in, on a well greased baking tray. Bake for 35-45 minutes until well risen and pale brown.

Remove from baking tray onto a wire rack. Make a small slit in the side to let the steam out, and leave until cold.

When ready to serve, whip cream until stiff but not solid.

Prepare fruit using 500g/1 lb of one fruit or a mixture of fruits. Rinse, hull and halve strawberries, rinse raspberries and green and black grapes or drain canned fruit well.

Reserve a little fruit to decorate, and fold the remainder into the whipped cream, sweetening with a little icing sugar to taste if using fresh fruit.

Put treasure chest on a serving plate, split open along one side and fill with fruit and cream, decorating with reserved fruits. Dredge top with icing sugar and serve.

Gâteau Saint Honoré

A showy and delicious French dessert.

Serves 6-8   *Preparation & cooking time: 1-1½ hours*

100g/4 oz shortcrust pastry made with butter (page 90)
2 tsp caster sugar
1 egg yolk – well beaten

Choux pastry:	**2 egg quantity (page 80)**
Filling:	**300g/½ pint Crème Patisserie (page 125), flavoured with vanilla or brandy**
	150g/¼ pint double cream – stiffly whipped
Caramel:	**100g/4 oz caster sugar**
To decorate:	**Fresh or sugar flowers, fruits or mint leaves**

Heat oven at 220°C/425°F/fan oven 200°C/gas 7-8. Make pastry as on page 90, adding sugar to rubbed in mixture and mixing pastry with beaten egg and cold water as needed. Roll pastry into a 20cm/8 in circle and place on a greased baking tray. Prick all over and dampen round edge with water.

Make choux pastry – see page 80. Put choux paste into a forcing bag with a wide, plain nozzle and pipe a ring of little buns round dampened edge of pastry base.

Using remaining paste, pipe the same number of buns onto another greased baking tray to use for the top ring of buns. Put both trays in the oven (pastry circle on upper shelf) and bake for 10 minutes. Lower heat to 190°C/375°F/fan oven 170°C/gas 5-6 for about 20 minutes until choux are risen and firm. Cool on wire racks, making a little steam slit in each bun.

To serve: Put pastry choux ring onto a large serving plate and fill all of the small buns with a little Crème Patisserie.

Put caster sugar in a small heavy pan over a low heat and stir carefully until melted and golden. Dip the base of each small filled bun into the caramel and stick onto the choux circle to make a ring, and dribble remaining caramel over the top. Fill ring with remaining Crème Patisserie, pipe the whipped cream on top and decorate with flowers, fruit or mint leaves.

Lemon Syllabub

Gorgeous and very rich. Serve syllabub the day it is made in stemmed wine glasses with Nutty Lemon Cookies (see page 126) or serve in Brandy Snap Baskets (see opposite). An even richer recipe which does not contain egg whites is given below.

NB As this syllabub contains raw egg it should not be given to young children, pregnant women or elderly people.

Serves 4-6   Preparation time: 15 minutes + chilling time

2 egg whites
100g/4 oz caster sugar
Juice of 1 lemon or 2 tbsp lemon juice
1 wine glass dry white wine or dry sherry
300ml/½ pint double cream
1 lemon for decoration

Put egg whites in a bowl or mixer and whisk until stiff.

Whisk in sugar a teaspoonful at a time, then gradually whisk in lemon juice, wine or sherry.

Whip cream until thick but still runny, pour it into the egg mixture and continue whisking until the syllabub is thick.

Pour into large wine glasses and chill in fridge until needed.

To serve: Make lemon twists for decoration – cut 6 thin rounds of lemon, cut nearly through to the centre and twist.

Put a twist of lemon on top of each syllabub, stand glass on a side plate and serve with a Nutty Lemon Cookie (see page 126).

Very Rich Lemon Syllabub (without egg white)

Use recipe above but omit egg whites, making a thick, smooth, cream. Whip cream and then gradually whip in sugar, lemon juice, wine or sherry, whisking as before until syllabub is thick and smooth. The wine or sherry can be omitted if preferred and extra lemon juice added to taste.

Filled Brandy Snap Baskets

Fun to serve for a special occasion, especially if children are present – you enjoy the filling and then eat the basket. They are best made and eaten the same day.

Makes 8-10 baskets Prep. & cooking time: about 45 minutes

50g/2 oz butter
50g/2 oz granulated or soft brown sugar
50g/2 oz golden syrup
½ tsp lemon juice
50g/2 oz plain flour and ½ tsp ground ginger

Heat oven at 170°C/325°F/fan oven 150°C/gas 3-4, and well grease 2 or 3 baking trays or cover with baking parchment. Grease the outside of several small basins, cups or ramekins to use as moulds for the baskets.

Put butter, sugar, syrup and lemon juice in a pan and melt over a low heat until completely dissolved. Remove pan from heat, sift flour and ginger together and stir into melted mixture, mixing well.

Put 2 small dessertspoonfuls of the mixture on a baking tray (only put one tray in the oven at a time so that they can be shaped easily) and bake for 7-8 minutes until golden brown. Remove tray from oven (put next tray in), leave to cool for a minute until firm enough to lift, and drape over basket moulds.

Continue until all the mixture is used, leaving baskets until firm before removing gently from moulds – they are very fragile.

Fill just before serving with fillings of choice – see below.

Lemon Syllabub – see opposite – fill baskets with syllabub and decorate with lemon twists.

Chocolate Mousse – see page 53 –fill baskets with mousse, decorate with whipped cream and grated chocolate.

Ice Cream – see 'Ice is Nice' or bought ice cream to taste. Put 2-3 scoops into each basket and top with whipped cream.

Hedingham Gardens Grape Pavlova

A party favourite with the party crowd when we lived near Plymouth. Crisp meringue with a soft, gooey centre, covered with a delicious creamy topping and dessert grapes.

Serves 6   *Prep. & cooking time: 1½ hours + cooling time*

Meringue Filling:
3 egg whites
175g/6 oz caster sugar
1 tsp cornflour
1 tsp vinegar
½ tsp vanilla essence

Filling:
100g/4 oz green grapes
100g/4 oz black grapes
1-2 tsp caster sugar
3-4 tbsp sherry
300m/½ pint double cream

Heat oven at 150°C/300°F/fan oven 140°C/gas 2-3.

Put egg whites in a bowl or mixer and whisk until stiff. Whisk in sugar a little at a time, mixing cornflour, vinegar and vanilla and whisking them in with the final spoonful of sugar.

Put a sheet of baking parchment on a baking tray, draw a 20cm/8 in circle on it (draw round a plate), and spread meringue on top, building up the sides to make a dish shape.

Bake for 1 hour, turn oven off and leave meringue inside to go quite cold, without opening the oven door – overnight is ideal! Peel off paper and store in an airtight container until needed.

Make filling: Rinse grapes, halve and de-pip, put into a bowl with sugar and sherry, and leave to soak for an hour. Strain grapes, put cream and sherry syrup into a bowl or mixer and whip until thick and stiff.

To serve: Place pavlova on serving plate, spread with the sherry cream and arrange grapes attractively on the top.

Raspberry or Strawberry Pavlova

Use raspberries or strawberries, and soak in white wine. Any suitable fresh or canned fruit can be used as a topping. Omit sherry or wine if preferred and top with plain whipped cream and fruit, or mix juice from canned fruit with the cream.

Jackie's Special Chocolate and Lemon Cheesecake

Another Plymouth party favourite. A deliciously lemony cheesecake on a chocolate biscuit base.

NB This recipe contains raw eggs and should not be given to very young children, pregnant women or elderly people.

Serves 8   Prep. & cooking time: 30 minutes + setting time

Base: **175g/6 oz chocolate wholemeal biscuits – crushed**
75g/3 oz butter – softened

Filling: **225g/8 oz full fat cream cheese**
50g/2 oz caster sugar
1 tsp vanilla essence
2 lemons – grated rind and juice
3 eggs – separated
12½g/1 packet gelatine
300ml/½ pint double cream
2-3 tbsp grated chocolate

Heat oven at 170°C/325°F/fan oven 150°C/ gas 3-4 and grease a 20cm/8 in loose-based cake tin or spring form tin.

Put biscuit crumbs and butter in a bowl and mix well. Press mixture onto base of tin and bake for 8-10 minutes. Remove from oven and leave in the tin, just loosening base when cold.

Put cream cheese, sugar, vanilla, lemon rind and juice and egg yolks in a bowl or mixer, and whisk together until creamy.

Dissolve gelatine in 2 tbsp hot water and whisk into mixture.

Whip cream until stiff and fold into creamy mixture.

Beat egg whites until stiff but not solid and fold gently into the mixture. Pour or spoon carefully into the cold tin over the biscuit crust, smooth top and leave to set in the fridge for 24 hours.

To serve: Unmould immediately before eating or it may collapse if left to stand for long! Take carefully out of tin, and slide onto a serving plate. Sprinkle top with grated chocolate, and serve with a jug of thick pouring cream if liked.

Coeur à la Crème

A very romantic dessert to serve at a Saint Valentine's dinner à deux – a rich creamy mixture made in little heart-shaped dishes, garnished with a few fresh raspberries or strawberries and served with a jug of Raspberry Satin Sauce. However, it's delicious served any time of year, and can be made just as successfully in little round ramekins.

NB This recipe contains raw egg and should not be served to young children, pregnant women or elderly people.

Serves 4-6 – depending on the size of the dishes

Preparation time: 30 minutes + overnight to drain and chill

225g/8 oz full fat cream cheese
300ml/½ pint thick double cream or full fat crème fraîche
50g/2 oz caster sugar – or to taste
2 egg whites

To serve: **100g/4 oz fresh raspberries or strawberries**
A little caster sugar to taste
Raspberry Satin Sauce – see page 120

Put cream cheese, thick double cream or crème fraîche and sugar in a bowl, and mix with a wooden spoon. Whisk egg whites until stiff, and fold into cream mixture.

Put a nylon sieve, or a wire sieve lined with a piece of muslin, over a bowl, spoon the cream mixture into the sieve and leave to drain overnight in the fridge.

About an hour before serving take drained cream mixture from the fridge, spoon into heart shaped or round ramekins, pressing down firmly and smoothing the top of each crème.

Put ramekins back in the fridge, and chill until ready to serve.

To serve: It may be possible to tip the crèmes out of the moulds onto plates, but it's safer to serve them in the dishes! Rinse raspberries or rinse, hull and halve strawberries, and arrange on top of crèmes, and sprinkle with sugar to taste.

Pour a little Raspberry Satin Sauce around edges of each crème, and serve remainder separately in a small jug.

Zabaglione

A smooth, rich Italian dessert, best served warm immediately it is made, as Zabaglione tends to separate if left to go cold.

NB Zabaglione contains raw egg and should not be served to young children, pregnant women or elderly people.

Serves 4   *Preparation time: 15 minutes*

3 egg yolks
75g/3 oz caster sugar
5 tbsp Marsala, sweet white wine or pale cream sherry or lemon juice

Put egg yolks and sugar in a thick heatproof bowl, whisk until well mixed and pale, then whisk in chosen wine or sherry.

Place bowl over a pan of simmering water and whisk until mixture is creamy and thick enough to leave a trail.

Pour into 4 long-stemmed wine glasses and serve at once, with langues de chat or thin sugar biscuits if liked.

Cold Creamy Zabaglione

The addition of whipped cream allows the Zabaglione to cool without separating, but should be eaten the same day.

Serves 4   *Preparation time: 30 minutes*

3 egg yolks
75g/3 oz caster sugar
5 tbsp Marsala, sweet white wine or pale cream sherry or lemon juice
150ml/¼ pint double cream

Whisk yolks, sugar and wine over water as above, until thick.

Remove bowl from heat, place in a bowl of ice or icy water and whisk until cold. Whip cream until thick and fold into the cold mixture. Pour into 4 long-stemmed wine glasses and chill until needed.

Strawberry Shortcake

An easy and pretty summer dessert. Make the shortcake in advance and assemble in a few minutes when ready to serve.

Serves 6-8   *Preparation & cooking time: 30-40 minutes*

Shortcake: **175g/6 oz butter – soft but not runny**
75g/3 oz caster sugar
175g/6 oz plain flour
75g/3 oz cornflour
1 egg yolk – well beaten with a fork

Topping: **300ml/½ pint double cream or Chantilly**
Crème – see page 124
450g/1 lb strawberries – rinsed and hulled
A few small mint leaves to decorate

Heat oven at 180°C/350°F/fan oven 160°C/gas 4-5. Grease two 18-20cm/7-8 in fluted sandwich cake tins, and line base with greased greaseproof paper or baking parchment.

Put butter and sugar in a bowl and beat until soft and creamy.

Gradually mix in flour and cornflour, adding a little egg yolk if needed but no water, to make a rollable dough, using your fingertips to work the mixture together into a ball.

Divide dough in half, roll out on a lightly floured surface into two circles to fit the tins, and slide dough into tins, pressing gently to fit right into the fluted edges. Prick well with a fork to stop the shortcake rising, and bake for 20-25 minutes, until a very pale golden, being careful not to let the shortcake get too brown.

Leave to cool for a few minutes in the tin, then tip onto a cooling tray and leave until cold. If not using immediately store in an airtight container until needed.

To serve: Whip cream until stiff or prepare Chantilly Crème. Slice strawberries, save a few to decorate and fold into cream.

Put one shortcake onto a serving plate and spread with half the mixture. Gently put the other shortcake on top and cover with remaining cream mixture. Decorate with whole berries and mint leaves and serve at once.

7

LIKE MOTHER MAKES

– or maybe even better!

Homemade Shortcrust Pastry

Shortcrust pastry can be bought ready made, chilled or frozen, but it's quick and easy to make (especially if you have a food processor) and it's much cheaper than the bought variety.

Makes 225g/8 oz – recipes usually give pastry required by the weight of flour used.   *Preparation time: 5 minutes*

When making shortcrust pastry, use half fat to flour, and allow approximately 1 tsp cold water to each 25g/1 oz flour.

225g/8 oz plain flour
Pinch salt
100g/4 oz butter, margarine or white cooking fat
8 tsp cold water

Sieve flour and salt into a mixing bowl. Grate or cut chosen fat into flour, and rub lightly together with fingertips until mixture looks like breadcrumbs.

Mix to a stiff dough with cold water (mix with a table knife), adding more water if needed, but don't get the dough too wet and sticky.

The dough is now ready to use, or it can be wrapped in plastic film and stored in the fridge or freezer until needed.

If using a food processor, follow the maker's instructions.

To make a Pastry Flan Case, 20-23cm/8-9in (baked blind)
Heat oven at 200°C/400°F/fan oven 180°C/gas 6-7. Make pastry as above, and roll out to a large enough piece to line flan tin or ring. Lift pastry over rolling pin and fit into flan case, pressing down gently to fit the shape. Prick all over with a fork, line flan tightly with foil and chill for 20 minutes.

Bake in the hot oven, for 10-15 minutes, removing foil for last 2-3 minutes, to crisp the inside of flan.

If using frozen pastry whether bought or homemade, allow plenty of time for defrosting before use.

Old-Fashioned Apple Pie

A deep pie dish filled with a juicy spiced apple filling, and topped with a traditional short pastry crust.

Serves 6   *Preparation & cooking time: 50-60 minutes*

175g/6 oz shortcrust pastry – see opposite
750g/1½ lb cooking apples – nice crisp Bramleys are good
100g/4 oz granulated sugar
¼ tsp cloves or all spice – optional
¼ tsp cinnamon and/or mixed spice – optional
Little milk for brushing

Heat oven at 200°C/400°F/fan oven 180°C/gas 6-7. Make pastry – see opposite – and put aside.

Peel, core and slice apples thinly, put into a 900ml/1½ pint deep pie dish and mix in sugar and chosen spices.

Roll out pastry a bit larger than pie dish, cut a 1cm/½ inch pastry strip to fit round rim, brush rim with milk and put strip onto the rim. Brush strip with milk and fit pastry lid on top, pressing edges together. Trim pastry and crimp edges.

Brush pie top with milk, sprinkle with sugar and bake in the hot oven for 30-35 minutes, reducing heat 180°C/350°F/fan oven 160°C/gas 4-5 if the pastry begins to look too brown. Serve hot, with lots of custard, whipped cream or ice cream.

Apple & Sultana Pie: Add 50g/2 oz sultanas with the apples.

Apple & Redcurrant Pie: Add 75g/3 oz currants with the apples.

Raspberry Pie: Add 250g/8 oz raspberries with the apples.

Gooseberry Pie: Use 750g/1½ lb gooseberries, topped and tailed, and 100-175g/4-6 oz sugar, or to taste.

Rhubarb Pie: Use 750g/1½ lb rhubarb, cut into 2cm/1 in lengths, 100-175g/4-6 oz sugar, or to taste.

Plum Pie: Use 750g/1½ lb plums, 100g/4 oz sugar, or to taste.

Apple and Blackberry Plate Pie

Bill, my husband's, favourite pie – if I had a fiver for every time I've made it I wouldn't need to buy a lottery ticket! There is a thin pastry layer under the fruit and a crisp, sugary top as well.

Serves 6   *Cooking & preparation time: 45-50 minutes*

225g/8 oz shortcrust pastry – see page 90
500g/1 lb cooking apples
Handful blackberries – fresh or frozen (no need to defrost)
100g/4 oz granulated sugar, plus 1 tbsp sugar for topping
A little milk for brushing

Heat oven at 200°C/400°F/fan oven 180°C/gas 6-7. Make shortcrust pastry, divide dough in half, roll one piece out on a floured surface and line a 20cm/8 in pie plate.

Peel, core and thinly slice apples, put them onto the pie plate, scatter blackberries on top, sprinkle on sugar and mix into the fruit. Brush edge of pastry crust with milk.

Roll out remaining pastry, slightly larger than the pie plate, drape pastry over rolling pin and lay top crust over pie. Trim edges, press together to seal, and crimp with a knife. Brush top of pastry with milk, and scatter liberally with sugar. Make a tiny steam hole in the middle of the pie with a pointed knife and stand pie on a baking tray. Bake in the hot oven for 20-25 minutes, until top is crisp and pale golden and serve warm or cold with custard or cream.

Turnovers

Use apples, apple and blackberries or jam. Make pastry as above, roll out and cut 6 circles, using a saucer as a pattern, re-rolling pastry scraps to use all the pastry.

Put a portion of prepared fruit on each round and top with 1-2 tsp sugar, or use 1-2 tbsp jam. Brush round pastry edges with milk, lift edges to meet, forming a ridge along the top and pinch together to seal. Put on a baking sheet, brush with milk and sprinkle with sugar. Bake as above in hot oven for 15-20 minutes. Serve warm with custard, or cold as part of a picnic.

Sunshine Syrup Tart

Just mention that it's treacle tart for pudding and enjoy the smiles that appear on the faces of all the men present!

Serves 6   *Preparation & cooking time: 30 minutes*

225g/8 oz shortcrust pastry – see page 90
About 1 teacup full of cornflakes
6-8 tbsp golden syrup (according to size of the spoonfuls)

Heat oven at 200°C/400°F/fan oven 180°C/gas 6-7. Make pastry – see page 90.

Roll pastry out thinly, lift it over the rolling pin and line a 20cm/8 in pie plate, pressing it to fit the shape of the plate.

Trim edges and cut to make a sun (make cuts all round pastry rim at 2.5cm/1 in intervals, damp pastry edge and fold the edges of the little squares inwards to make points, pressing together and crimping with a small pointed knife).

Cover pastry with slightly crushed cornflakes and spoon syrup over the top, covering cornflakes completely.

Bake in the hot oven for 8-10 minutes until pastry is cooked. Serve warm with cream, custard or crème fraîche.

Traffic Light Tart

225g/8 oz pastry – see page 90
4 large tbsp of each jam – strawberry, apricot, greengage

Make pastry and line a 23cm/9 in pie plate as above. Roll out trimmings, cut into 1cm/½ in strips. Damp ends, twist across tart to form 6 triangles, securing ends on pastry rim.

Fill each triangle with coloured jam in traffic light sequence.

Bake in the hot oven as above, for 8-10 minutes.

Serve warm or cold, with custard, cream or crème fraîche.

Lemon Meringue Pie

A lovely lemony filling to contrast with the sweet meringue, or try the apple filling given below. Calorie counters can omit flan case and put filling into a pie dish with meringue on top.

Serves 4-6   *Preparation & cooking time: 1-1½ hours*

20cm/8 in pastry flan case – see page 90

Filling: **2 tbsp cornflour**
               2-3 lemons – grated rind and juice
               300ml/½ pint water
               3 egg yolks
               75g/3 oz caster sugar – or to taste

Meringue: **3 egg whites**
               175g/6 oz caster sugar

Prepare and bake a 20cm/8 in pastry flan case – see page 90. Then lower oven heat to 150°C/300°F/fan oven 140°C/gas 2-3.

Make filling: Put cornflour and lemon rind into a pan, and mix to a runny paste with the lemon juice. Stir in water, put pan over a low heat stirring until sauce is thick and smooth, then remove pan from heat. Whisk egg yolks and beat into lemon sauce with sugar to taste. Pour mixture into prepared flan case.

Make meringue: Whisk egg whites in a large bowl until stiff, then gradually whisk in sugar. Spoon meringue over flan, and bake in a low oven for 20-30 minutes, until crisp and golden.

Serve warm or cold, with thickly whipped cream.

Apple Meringue Pie

A delicious way to use windfalls.

450g/1 lb cooking apples – peeled, cored and sliced
1 lemon – grated rind and juice
3 egg yolks
2-4 oz caster sugar – to taste

Put apples, lemon rind and juice in a pan, cook over low heat for 10-15 minutes until apples are soft. Remove from heat. Whisk egg yolks and beat into apples, adding sugar to taste. Pour into pastry case, cover with meringue and cook as above.

Raspberry or Cranberry Linzertorte

A gorgeous rich torte from Austria, made with sweet almond or hazelnut pastry topped with a red fruit filling.

Serves 6   *Prep. & cooking time: 1½ hours + chilling time*

Pastry: **175g/6 oz plain flour**
¼ tsp mixed spice
75g/3 oz ground hazelnuts or ground almonds
75g/3 oz caster sugar
75g/3 oz butter
1 egg – well beaten

Filling: **454g can raspberries or 454g jar cranberry sauce**
1 tbsp arrowroot or cornflour
1 tbsp caster sugar – or to taste

Glaze: **3 tbsp redcurrant jelly**

Make pastry: Put flour, spice, ground hazelnuts or almonds and caster sugar into a bowl, and rub in butter to make a crumbly mixture. Mix in beaten egg, knead gently to make a soft dough and form into a ball. Cover with plastic film and chill.

Make filling: Put raspberries and juice, or cranberry sauce, into a small pan. Mix arrowroot or cornflour to a thin paste with a little of the fruit juice and mix it into the fruit. Heat mixture gently over a low heat, stirring until it comes to the boil, then reduce heat and simmer for a few moments until the filling thickens. Remove from heat and leave to cool.

Heat oven at 190°C/375°F/fan oven 170°C/gas 5-6.

Take pastry from fridge, save a small lump of dough for the lattice topping, and press flan dough into a 20-23cm/8-9 in flan tin or ring, placed on a baking sheet.

Pour cooled filling into the flan, roll out reserved dough, cut into 1cm/½ in wide strips and use to make a lattice across on top of filling, dampening ends with water to seal. Bake for 25-35 minutes, and cool before removing flan ring.

Melt redcurrant jelly and brush over top of pastry lattice. Serve warm or cold, with cream or Almond Chantilly Crème.

Yorkshire Curd Tart

A deep, creamy spiced tart. Different versions can be found throughout the Ridings of the White Rose, but this recipe was approved by Rowena, my Yorkshire nearly daughter-in-law from Scarborough.

Serves 6-8   *Preparation & cooking time: 45-55 minutes*

225g/8 oz shortcrust pastry, made with butter – see page 90
1 tbsp caster sugar
2 egg yolks – well beaten

Filling: **450g/1 lb curd cheese**
            175g/6 oz granulated sugar
            175g/6 oz sultanas
            ¼ tsp cinnamon and/or mixed spice
            A good grate of nutmeg
            Grated rind of 1 lemon
            ½ tsp vanilla essence
            2 eggs
            50g/2 oz butter – melted

Heat oven at 190°C/375°F/fan oven 170°C/gas 5-6.

Make pastry, as on page 90, adding the sugar to the rubbed in flour and butter mixture, and mixing the pastry with the beaten egg and a little cold water as needed.

Line a 20-23cm/8-9 in deep flan tin or shallow loose-based cake tin 6cm/2-3 in deep – see page 90 – and leave in the fridge to rest, while you prepare the filling; do not bake yet.

Put curd cheese, sugar, sultanas, spices, nutmeg and lemon rind into a bowl.

Beat eggs with vanilla essence and stir into curd mixture with melted butter, and mix well.

Stand flan tin on a baking sheet, pour filling into prepared flan case, and bake for 20-30 minutes until filling is just set.

Allow to cool, then remove from flan or cake tin. Serve warm or cold.

Lancashire Apple Pie

Across the Pennines in the Red Rose county, this tasty variation of apple pie is a real treat. Cheese and apple cooked together may seem a strange mixture, but it is also a tradition in the North East where a good slice of strong Cheddar is the usual accompaniment to a piece of apple pie.

Serves 6   *Preparation & cooking time: about 1 hour*

225g/8 oz shortcrust pastry – see page 90

Filling: **500g/1 lb sharp cooking apples – Bramleys if possible**
100g/4 oz demerara sugar
½ tsp cinnamon and/or mixed spice
100g/4 oz Lancashire Cheese

Top: **1 egg white – beaten**
1 heaped tbsp demerara sugar

Heat oven at 200°C/400°F/fan oven 180°C/gas 6-7. Make pastry: Divide dough in half, roll one piece out on a floured board and line a 23cm/9 in pie plate.

Peel, core and slice apples thinly. Put half of the apples into the pie plate and scatter with half of the sugar and a pinch of spice. Crumble cheese into lumps, and scatter half the cheese on top of sugar.

Repeat the layers again, using up all the filling.

Roll out remaining pastry as thinly as possible, to make a nice thin crust, dampen edges of flan case with water, and cover with the pastry lid – it doesn't matter if the top looks lumpy. Trim edges, press together to seal and crimp with a knife.

Brush top of pie with beaten egg white, and sprinkle liberally with demerara sugar. Make a tiny steam hole in the middle of the crust with a pointed knife.

Stand pie on a baking tray, and bake in the hot oven for 25-30 minutes, until pastry is golden brown and filling is soft.

Serve warm or cold, with thickly whipped cream.

Tarte aux Fruits

A lovely summer dessert, topped with fresh or canned fruit as you like. The flan case and crème patisserie can be made in advance, but the tarte should be served soon after filling with crème and fruit.

Serves 6   *Prep. time: 15 minutes + time making flan case*
and crème patisserie – see pages 90 and 125

225g/8 oz shortcrust pastry, made with butter – see page 90
1 tbsp caster sugar
2 egg yolks – well beaten
300ml/½ pint quantity Creme Patisserie – see page 125

Fruit of choice:
500g/1 lb strawberries – rinsed, hulled and halved
500g/1 lb raspberries – rinsed and picked over
454g can sliced peaches or apricot halves – drained
100g/4 oz each green and black seedless grapes – rinsed
** or any combination of fruit to choice**

Glaze:
100g/4 oz redcurrant jelly – if using red fruit
100g/4 oz apricot jam if using yellow or pale fruit

Make pastry, as on page 90, adding the sugar to the rubbed in flour and butter mixture and mixing pastry with the beaten egg and a little cold water as needed.

Line a 20-23cm/8-9 in flan case, and bake blind – see page 90.

Prepare Crème Patisserie. Prepare chosen fruit.

Not more than a few hours before serving, place the cold flan case on a serving plate and fill with cold Crème Patisserie. Arrange the chosen fruit (all the same kind or a mixture of several) attractively on top of the crème.

Put appropriate jam or jelly in a small pan, melt over a very low heat and brush carefully over the top of the tarte, covering all the fruit and the pastry rim and leave to set.

Serve tarte alone or with a jug of pouring cream if preferred.

Holzgerlingen Creamy Mandarin Flan

A recipe from my daughter-in-law Barbara in Germany where large cakes are very popular. Make this recipe for a party or use a smaller flan case and halve the ingredients for a family dessert.

Large flan serves 12-16   *Prep. & cooking time: 1½ hours*
Smaller flan serves 6-8   *Prep. & cooking time: 1¼ hours*

225g/8 oz (large) or 175g/6 oz (small) shortcrust pastry
500g/1 lb fromage frais
150g/5 oz granulated sugar
2 eggs – beaten
1 packet/2 tbsp vanilla blancmange or custard powder
100ml/4 fl oz sour cream or crème fraîche
75ml/3 fl oz vegetable oil
250ml/8 fl oz milk
300g can mandarin oranges
1 orange or lemon jelly

Heat oven at 180°C/350°F/fan oven 160°C/gas 4-5. Make pastry (see page 90) and line a 28cm/11 in or 20-22cm/8-9 in spring form tin, 6cm/2-3 in deep. Put flan case to chill in fridge – do not bake yet.

Mix fromage frais, sugar and beaten eggs in a large bowl.

In another bowl whisk blancmange or custard powder with sour cream or crème fraîche and oil, add milk, and pour mixture into the other ingredients in the large bowl, mixing well.

Stand flan case on a baking tray, and pour filling in carefully.

Drain mandarins, saving juice, and arrange fruit on top of flan. Bake for 50-60 minutes (large flan) or 30-40 minutes (small flan), until pastry is golden and filling is firm. Leave to cool.

Make jelly according to instructions on the packet, adding mandarin juice with the cold water. Leave in fridge or freezer until beginning to set.

Take flan from tin and put on a serving plate. Spoon setting jelly over the top, and leave to set completely before serving.

Bakewell Pudding

Traditionally called a pudding, but really a lovely tart – please don't giggle! There are lots of local variations, but this recipe tastes delicious whatever you call it. Use short or puff pastry to make the flan case, according to personal preference.

Serves 6   *Preparation & cooking time: 45-55 minutes*

**175g/6 oz shortcrust pastry – see page 90 or 225g/8 oz
  pack of frozen puff pastry – completely thawed
3-4 tbsp raspberry jam (traditionally a red jam filling, but
  use apricot if you prefer)
100g/4 oz butter
100g/4 oz granulated sugar
75g/3 oz ground rice
50g/2 oz ground almonds
2 eggs
½ tsp almond essence**

Heat oven at 200°C/400°F/fan oven 180°C/gas 6-7. Prepare and roll out chosen pastry, and line a 20-23cm/8-9 in flan dish or flan ring – see page 90.

Spread jam over pastry base and leave to chill in fridge while you prepare the rest of the filling.

Melt butter in a pan over a low heat, add sugar and stir until sugar has melted.

Remove from heat and mix in ground rice and ground almonds.

Beat eggs and almond essence together, and stir into filling.

Stand flan dish or case on a baking sheet and spoon or pour filling into pastry case on top of the jam.

Bake for 30-35 minutes until filling is well risen, set and golden, covering lightly with foil if top becomes too brown.

Remove flan ring if used, and serve pudding warm or cold – traditionally on its own, but you can add cream if you wish!

Gypsy Tart

I've no idea what connection this gorgeous pastry-based flan has with the gypsies, but it's a pudding that I remember from my own school dinner days, when it was a universal favourite amidst a lot of very unpopular fifties school dinner dishes! It's now enjoying a fashionable revival, so do try it.

Serves 6　　　　　　　　　　*Preparation time: 40-45 minutes*
+ chilling time for evaporated milk – leave in fridge overnight

175g/6 oz shortcrust pastry
405g can evaporated milk – well chilled in fridge
350g/12 oz soft brown sugar
½ tsp vanilla essence

Heat oven at 200°C/400°F/fan oven 180°C/gas oven 6-7.

Make pastry and line a 20-23cm/8-9 in flan tin or ring, and bake blind – see page 90. Remove from oven and leave to cool in the flan ring.

Put evaporated milk, soft brown sugar and vanilla essence in a bowl and whisk (preferably with an electric mixer) until mixture forms a thick, creamy batter. This will take 10-15 minutes, although chilled evaporated milk whips faster than milk at room temperature.

Pour filling into baked pastry case, and bake for 8-10 minutes until pastry edges are brown, but the filling will still feel soft.

Remove flan from the oven, being careful not to spill the runny filling.

Leave to cool for 10 minutes, so that the filling can set.

Remove from flan case and slide onto a serving plate.

As the Gypsy Tart is very sweet, it is nice served with crème fraîche – although at school dinners we ate it on its own and thought it was wonderful!

Tarte Tatin

A delicious upside down fruit tarte, originally from France, lovely served warm with cream, or cold as a picnic dessert.

Serves 4-6   *Preparation & cooking time: 50-60 minutes*

25g/1 oz butter
75g/3 oz dark soft brown sugar
½ tsp mixed spice, cinnamon or all spice
500g/1 lb sweet dessert apples
100g/4 oz shortcrust pastry, made with butter – see page 90

Heat oven at 180°C/350°F/fan oven 160°C/gas 4-5. Melt butter and well grease base and sides of a 20cm/8 in solid-based sponge sandwich tin, then line base of tin with a circle of well buttered greaseproof paper or baking parchment.

Mix brown sugar with chosen spice and spread evenly over the base of the tin.

Peel, core and slice apples, and arrange in circles in the tin on top of the sugar.

Roll pastry into a circle about 1 cm/½ in thick, and cut to fit the top of the tin exactly. Carefully cover apples with the pastry lid, pressing it down gently to fit on top of the fruit.

Bake for 35-40 minutes, until fruit is cooked and pastry is pale golden, covering tin lightly with foil if pastry browns too quickly.

Remove from oven and leave to cool for 10 minutes, then loosen edges and turn upside down onto a serving plate.

Serve hot or cold with thick pouring cream or crème fraîche.

Apricot Tarte Tatin

Lovely when fresh apricots are in season. Use 500g/1 lb fresh apricots, washed and stoned, instead of apples, and prepare and serve as above.

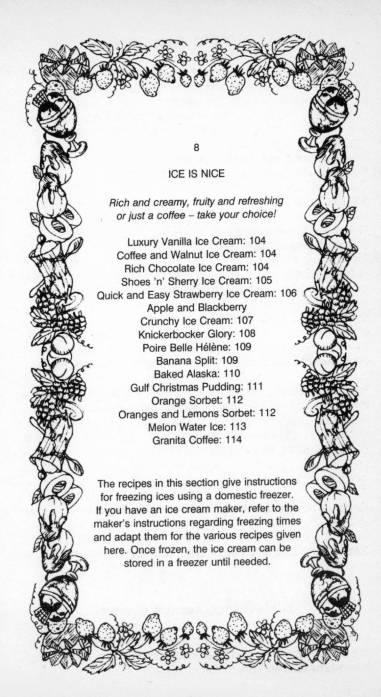

8

ICE IS NICE

*Rich and creamy, fruity and refreshing
or just a coffee – take your choice!*

The recipes in this section give instructions
for freezing ices using a domestic freezer.
If you have an ice cream maker, refer to the
maker's instructions regarding freezing times
and adapt them for the various recipes given
here. Once frozen, the ice cream can be
stored in a freezer until needed.

Luxury Vanilla Ice Cream

A really creamy tasting ice cream, easy to make without an ice cream maker, as it does not need any further attention once mixed and put into the freezer.

NB These recipes contain raw eggs and should not be given to very young children, pregnant women or elderly people.

Makes about 1 litre/2 pints ice cream
Preparation time: 10 minutes + freezing time

4 eggs, separated
100g/4 oz icing sugar
½ tsp vanilla essence
300ml/½ pint double cream

Put egg whites into a large bowl and whisk until stiff. Sieve icing sugar and whisk into egg whites a teaspoonful at a time.

Put egg yolks and vanilla essence into a smaller bowl and whisk until creamy, then fold gently into the egg whites.

Whip cream until thick but not solid and fold into egg mixture.

Pour into a plastic container, cover and freeze until needed – the ice cream will take 3-4 hours to become solid.

Remove from freezer and leave to soften for 10-15 minutes in fridge or a cool kitchen before serving.

Coffee and Walnut Ice Cream

Add 3 tbsp strong black coffee and 100g/4 oz finely chopped walnuts and fold into egg mixture with the cream.

Rich Chocolate Ice Cream

Melt 100g/4 oz plain cooking chocolate in a bowl over a pan of simmering water, and beat into whisked egg yolks before folding mixture into the stiff egg whites.

Shoes 'n' Sherry Ice Cream

For adults only – but you could omit the sherry and make a delicious fruity ice cream for children. Named for a special friend who loves new shoes and enjoys a good sherry!

Serves 6-8   *Preparation time: 20 minutes*
          + 1 hour pre-soaking time and freezing time

175g/6 oz dried tropical fruit mix, raisins or sultanas
150ml/¼ pint pale sweet sherry
1 litre/2 pints custard – made using custard powder and full cream milk as directed on packet, or bought ready to use in cans or cartons which is much easier!
50g/2 oz caster sugar
300ml/½ pint double cream

Chop tropical fruit into small even-sized pieces if used. Put chosen fruit into a bowl with the sherry and leave to soak for 1-2 hours or overnight.

Make custard as directed if homemade, and pour into a cold, clean bowl, or pour ready prepared custard into a bowl.

Stir in sugar – this is extra to the sugar that is used in homemade custard.

Stir soaked fruit and sherry into custard.

Whip cream until thick but not stiff, and fold it into custard.

Pour mixture into a plastic container, cover and leave in freezer for 2-2½ hours until just beginning to freeze.

Tip into bowl and beat until creamy, pour back into plastic container and leave to freeze completely.

To serve: Remove ice cream from freezer and leave to soften in fridge or a cool kitchen for 15-20 minutes.

Spoon into glass dishes and pour a little extra sherry over the top if liked.

Quick and Easy Strawberry Ice Cream

A delicious creamy summer ice cream, good to make when strawberries are plentiful and cheap. It has the advantage that it does not contain raw eggs, and so is suitable for those who have to avoid them.

Makes 2 litres/3½ pints ice cream

Preparation time: 15 minutes + freezing time

350g/12 oz granulated sugar
600ml/1 pint water
1kg/2 lb fresh strawberries
600ml/1 pint double cream

Put sugar and water in a heavy-based pan, bring to the boil and stir until sugar is dissolved.

Boil gently for 8-10 minutes to make about 600ml/1pint thin syrup and remove from heat.

Rinse and hull strawberries, and purée in a processor, or chop roughly and mash well with a potato masher.

Stir syrup into strawberry purée, mix well, pour into a lidded plastic container and freeze for 2-3 hours until just beginning to freeze.

Tip strawberry mixture into a large bowl and whip until creamy.

Whip cream until thick but not solid, and whip into strawberries a spoonful at a time.

Return ice cream to plastic container, cover with lid and freeze until needed.

To serve: Remove ice cream from freezer and leave to soften in fridge or a cool kitchen for 15-20 minutes.

Apple and Blackberry Crunchy Ice Cream

NB This contains raw egg and should not be given to very young children, pregnant women or elderly people.

Serves 6-8   *Preparation time: 30 minutes + freezing time*

Apple Mousse
750g/1½ lb cooking apples
3-4 tbsp water or cider
100-175g/4-6 oz granulated
  sugar

Blackberry Mousse
250g/½ lb blackberries
1-2 tbsp water
50-75g/2-3 oz granulated
  sugar

Keep the two fruits separate.

3 egg whites
600ml/1 pint double cream
6-8 meringue shells
To decorate: **a little crème de cassis – optional**

Peel, core and slice apples, simmer gently in a pan with water or cider for 5-10 minutes, until soft. Pour into a processor or liquidiser and blend. Put fruit mixture through a nylon sieve to make a smooth purée, sweeten to taste and leave to cool.

Wash blackberries, cook, blend, sieve and sweeten as above to make a wonderful dark velvety purée.

Whip egg whites until stiff, and fold two thirds into the apple purée and one third into the blackberry. Whip cream until thick but not solid, and fold three-quarters into the apple mixture and a quarter into the blackberry mix.

Pour each mousse into a plastic container, cover and freeze for 1-2 hours until half frozen. Remove from freezer and beat each mousse until soft and mushy.

Crumble meringues slightly and mix into blackberry mousse, then using a metal spoon, fold blackberry mix into the apple mouse, swirling gently to give a ripple effect. Pour mixture gently into a lidded plastic container and freeze until needed.

To serve: Leave to soften for 15-20 minutes in fridge or cool kitchen, then scoop into sundae dishes or large wine glasses.

Pour a little crème de cassis over each serving if liked.

Knickerbocker Glory

Lovely to eat outside on a warm afternoon. Use tall, clear glasses, and fill with jelly, fresh or canned fruit and ice creams to make a gloriously colourful dessert.

Serves 6   Preparation time: 15 minutes + jelly setting time

135g packet raspberry or strawberry jelly
300ml/½ pint Raspberry Satin Sauce – see page 120

Choose a selection of fruit:
2 ripe fresh peaches or nectarines, peeled stoned and
  sliced
Small can peaches in syrup
Small bunch green seedless grapes
2 ripe Comice pears, cored, peeled and sliced
Small can pears, sliced
Small can mixed fruit salad
Small can pineapple rings in juice or syrup
2 bananas, cut into slices

150ml/¼ pint whipped double cream or aerosol cream
600ml/1 pint vanilla and/or raspberry ripple ice cream
6 glacé cherries

Put jelly in measuring jug and dissolve in 150ml/¼ pint boiling water. Drain any canned fruit and add juice or syrup to jelly. Make up to 600ml/1 pint with cold water or ice cubes and leave to set in fridge or freezer.

Prepare Raspberry Satin sauce. Prepare fruit. Whip cream and put into a piping bag, if liked.

When set, chop jelly and put 1-2 tbsp in each glass.

Put a small layer of fruit on top of jelly, mixing the different fruits, add a tablespoonful of ice cream and pour over a little raspberry sauce.

Repeat the layers until the glasses are full, finishing with a scoop of ice cream. Top each sundae with a big rosette or swirl of cream, and pop the traditional cherry on the top of each Knickerbocker Glory.

Poire Belle Hélène

A posh name for pears and ice cream in hot chocolate sauce, scrumptious for dessert on a hot summer day! You can use fresh poached pears if you wish, but who wants to stand at the stove cooking when the sun's shining, so cheat, use canned pears and enjoy them in the garden.

Serves 4   *Preparation & cooking time: 15 minutes*

Chocolate Sauce to taste – see page 116 or 117
4 scoops vanilla ice cream
4 scoops chocolate ice cream
4 canned or pre-poached pears

To serve:
Mary's Chocolate Chip Cookies – see page 126 – or small, sweet dessert biscuits

Make chosen chocolate sauce and keep warm.

Put a scoop of each flavour ice cream in 4 wide sundae dishes.

Cut pears in half, and arrange two pear halves over the ice cream in each dish.

Spoon warm chocolate sauce over pears and serve at once with the chosen cookies or biscuits.

Banana Split

Substitute 4 large bananas, ripe but not soft, instead of pears.

Place two scoops ice cream in 4 long, gondola dishes, peel and split the bananas lengthways and then arrange banana halves along each side of the ice cream scoops.

Pour warm chocolate sauce over the ice cream, decorate with a ribbon of thickly whipped cream or aerosol cream and sprinkle a teaspoonful of grated mixed nuts along the top.

Serve at once.

Baked Alaska

A favourite party pudding of the seventies and now becoming popular at a new generation of dinner parties. The pudding has to be assembled and cooked at the very last minute, or it can be prepared completely (see below) and frozen in advance, then cooked from frozen just before serving.

Serves 6
Preparation time: 10 minutes   *Cooking time: 3-4 minutes*

1 × 20cm/8 in sponge flan case, see page 24, or shop bought
Either: 225g/8 oz fresh raspberries or strawberries with a little caster sugar to taste and (optional) 4 tbsp sherry or sweet dessert wine
Or: 4-5 tbsp raspberry or strawberry jam
3 egg whites
175g/6 oz caster sugar
450ml/¾ pint vanilla ice cream – homemade or bought

Make sponge case if necessary and allow to cool.

Put raspberries or hulled, sliced strawberries in a bowl with sugar to taste and sherry or wine if used, and leave to soak.

Heat oven at 230°C/450°F/fan oven 210°C/gas 8-9.

Make meringue: Beat egg whites until stiff, then whisk in sugar a little at a time. Put to one side.

Spoon fruit over flan case or spread thickly with jam. Pile ice cream on top, smoothing with a palette knife. Cover ice cream and sponge flan completely with a mound of meringue, making sure that the edges are sealed.

Bake in the hot oven for 3-4 minutes until meringue is set and a light golden brown. Serve at once.

To freeze in advance: Make up pudding, using jam not fruit, cover with the ice cream and meringue and open freeze.

To serve: Cook from frozen in the hot oven for 5-6 minutes until flan is defrosted and meringue is golden brown.

Gulf Christmas Pudding

An icy cold Christmas Pudding, ideal not only in the Middle East but in any country where December is lovely and warm. Perhaps not recommended for carrying to the beach, but great on Christmas Day after the traditional turkey, or in the garden after a barbecue, and in cooler climes a super summer dessert.

Serves 6   *Preparation time: 20 minutes*
                              + soaking and freezing time

75g/3 oz mixed tropical dried fruits, chopped
50g/2 oz sultanas
50g/2 oz stoneless raisins
50g/2 oz glacé cherries, chopped
50g/2 oz chopped pecan nuts or walnuts
25g/1 oz chopped mixed peel
3-4 tbsp brandy, rum, sweet sherry or fresh orange juice
Luxury Vanilla Ice Cream – see page 104
Grated rind of 1 orange
1 tsp mixed spice
½ tsp cinnamon
A good pinch of freshly grated nutmeg

To decorate:
Whipped double cream or aerosol cream
Glacé cherries, pecan nuts and/or walnuts
Sprig of holly and a sparkler – wipe the wire

Put all the fruits and nuts into a bowl with the brandy, rum, sherry or orange juice, cover and leave to soak overnight.

Prepare Luxury Vanilla Ice Cream – see page 104 – but leave mixture in the mixing bowl and do not freeze.

Stir soaked fruit and juice into the ice cream, with orange rind and spices and stir for luck! Spoon into a 1 litre/2 pint basin, cover and freeze until needed.

To serve: Dip basin into hot water for a few moments and upturn onto a serving dish. Decorate with piped, whipped cream or aerosol cream, glacé cherries and nuts and pop a sprig of holly on the top. For fun, stick a lighted sparkler on the top as well.

Orange Sorbet

This is like eating a really fruity orange lolly from a spoon –
very refreshing on a hot day!

NB The sorbets contain raw eggs and should not be given
to very young children, pregnant women or elderly people.

Serves 4   *Preparation time: 15 minutes + freezing time*

75g/3 oz caster sugar
Grated rind and juice of two oranges
A little 'breakfast orange juice' (from a carton) or water
185g can concentrated frozen orange juice
2 egg whites

Put sugar in a pan with grated orange rind, squeeze orange
juice into a measure and make up to 300ml/½ pint with
'breakfast orange juice' or water.

Heat slowly until sugar has dissolved, stirring occasionally.

Remove from heat, stir in frozen orange juice, pour mixture
into a plastic container and freeze for about 45 minutes until
crunchy and beginning to set.

Whip egg whites until stiff.

Take orange mixture from freezer, mash with a potato
masher until mushy and then fold egg whites into sorbet.
Pour into the lidded container and freeze until needed.

Remove from freezer 20-30 minutes before serving. Leave to
soften in fridge or cool kitchen.

Serve scoops of sorbet in sundae dishes or tall wine glasses
and top with fresh orange slices.

Lemon Sorbet

Replace fresh orange rind and juice with fresh lemons, and
use lemon juice instead of 'breakfast orange' or water. Taste
mixture before freezing, and stir in extra caster sugar to taste.

Melon Water Ice

The water ice looks pretty frozen and served in the melon shells, but it can be frozen in a plastic container and served scooped into sundae dishes if preferred.

NB This contains raw eggs and should not be given to very young children, pregnant women or elderly people.

Serves 4 in the melon shells or 6 if scooped into dishes

Preparation time: 15 minutes + freezing time

225g/8 oz caster sugar
Grated rind and juice of 1 orange
Grated rind and juice of 2 lemons
A little cold water
2 Galia, Ogen or Charentais melons
2 egg whites

Put sugar in a pan with grated orange and lemon rind. Squeeze orange and lemon juice into a measuring jug, make up to 300ml/½ pint with cold water and add to sugar. Bring to the boil, stirring until sugar is dissolved, then simmer for 5-10 minutes to make a thin syrup. Remove from heat.

Cut melons in half and remove all the seeds. Carefully spoon out the melon flesh, leaving just enough inside the shells to keep their shape. Put melon flesh in a processor or liquidiser and purée. Stir melon purée into the syrup, mix well and pour into a plastic box and freeze for about 1 hour until just getting crunchy.

Whip egg whites until stiff. Take melon purée from freezer and mash or whisk until mushy. Fold egg whites into water ice, mixing carefully.

Spoon water ice into the melon shells, wrap in plastic film, stand the filled shells upright in a wide plastic container and freeze until needed, or freeze the water ice in the plastic box.

To serve: Allow to soften in fridge or cool kitchen for 30-45 minutes. Place melon shells, or scoops of melon ice, in sundae glasses and decorate with tiny mint leaves.

Granita Coffee

Serve this delicious Italian crunchy iced coffee after the cheese course at the end of a dinner party.

Serves 4-6   Preparation time: 10 minutes + freezing time

4-6 heaped tbsp Continental blend ground coffee
4 heaped tbsp demerara, golden or white or granulated sugar – to taste
600ml/1 pint boiling water

To serve: **150ml/¼ pint whipped double cream – optional**

Put ground coffee and sugar into a large heatproof jug, using demerara, golden or white sugar as you prefer.

Measure in the boiling water, stir well until sugar is dissolved, cover jug and leave liquid to cool completely.

Strain coffee mixture through a fine nylon strainer into a plastic container, cover and freeze until frozen hard, about 2-3 hours.

Take frozen mix from the freezer, tip into a strong bowl or metal saucepan, and break mixture into small chunks to form the granita – use the end of a rolling pin or chop with a (very well washed) steak tenderiser. Do not bash too much, as the granita should be a coarse crystal texture when served.

Tip ice back into the plastic container, cover and freeze until needed.

Serve straight from the freezer, do not leave to soften.

Spoon granita into large wine glasses or small sundae coupes, and serve at once.

If liked, pour a little whipped cream over the top, or hand a jug of whipped cream separately.

For convenience, substitute 4-6 heaped tsp Continental blend instant coffee instead of ground coffee. Add chosen sugar, dissolve in boiling water and leave to cool. There is no need to strain the coffee before freezing the Granita.

9

SAUCY SAUCES,
CREAMY CRÈMES AND COOKIES

*Lovely accompaniments
to complement your puddings.*

Hot Chocolate Sauce

A lovely chocolatey sauce, yummy poured over homemade ice cream, Poire Belle Hélène or banana splits, or served with chocolate sponge puddings, flans or chocolate cakes.

Serves 4-6   *Preparation time: 10 minutes*

175g/6 oz plain cooking chocolate
2 heaped tbsp soft pale brown sugar
3-4 tbsp cold water
50g/2 oz unsalted butter
½ tsp vanilla essence

Put chocolate, sugar and water into a small pan, and stir over a low heat until sugar has melted and mixture is smooth and creamy.

Remove pan from heat. Cut butter into pieces and beat into sauce a little at a time.

Add vanilla essence and beat well to make a shiny sauce. Serve at once, or cover and put aside until needed.

Reheat sauce over a pan of hot water (not over direct heat or it may burn), stirring until runny, smooth and warm.

Chocolate Rum, Brandy or Whisky Sauce

Beat in 1 tbsp chosen spirit with the vanilla essence.

Chocolate Orange Sauce

Add grated rind and juice of 1 orange with the vanilla essence.

Nutty Chocolate Sauce

Add 1 heaped tbsp chopped mixed nuts with the vanilla essence.

Chocolate Cream Sauce

An instant sauce to turn plain ice cream or fruit sundaes into a feast!

Serves 4-6   *Preparation time: 10 minutes*

175g/6 oz plain cooking chocolate
150ml/¼ pint double cream or crème fraîche

Break chocolate into pieces, put into a small basin with the cream or crème fraîche.

Put basin over a pan of simmering water and stir until the chocolate has melted.

Remove from heat and beat to make a lovely smooth sauce.

Use at once, poured over ice creams or hot chocolate puddings.

Delicious variations of this sauce can be made using flavoured dessert chocolate bars – orange, coffee, mixed fruit, chopped nut and honey etc., or soft chocolate nougat and caramel bars instead of the cooking chocolate.

Chocolatey Whipped Cream

Lovely with chocolate puddings and so quick to make.

Serves 4-6   *Preparation time: 5 minutes*

150ml/¼ pint double cream
2 tsp sweetened drinking chocolate

Put cream into a bowl or mixer and gradually whip in the drinking chocolate at a slow speed.

Whip cream until thick but not solid and spoon into a small serving dish.

Fudgy Chocolate Filling or Topping

A rich, thick, fudgy chocolate filling or topping – I usually make double quantity and spread it on extra thick!

Fills a chocolate roulade or tops a 20cm/8 in cake

Preparation time: 15 minutes + 1 hour setting time

75g/3 oz caster sugar
75ml/3 fl oz evaporated milk
100g/4 oz plain cooking chocolate or chocolate chips
25g/1 oz unsalted butter
Few drops vanilla or almond essence

Put sugar and evaporated milk into a large heavy-based pan, put over a low heat and stir with a wooden spoon until sugar is completely dissolved.

Bring sauce slowly to the boil, then lower heat to the merest simmer and leave pan over the low heat for 5-6 minutes (7-8 minutes for double quantity) without stirring, until sauce becomes a lovely butterscotch syrup.

Remove pan from heat, beat in chocolate (broken into pieces), butter and vanilla or almond essence.

Pour into a bowl, cover with plastic film and leave in fridge for about an hour until thick enough to spread. If you are in a hurry, put the cold basin in the freezer to save time.

When set, stir well to make a smooth chocolate mixture and spread over roulade or cake.

The filling can be cooked in the microwave:

Put sugar and evaporated milk into a large heatproof bowl and cook on HIGH/power 10 for 2-3 minutes (3-4 minutes for double quantity) until sugar is dissolved – the sauce will rise in the bowl as it cooks.

Then cook on LOW/power 3 for about 3-4 minutes (7-8 minutes double quantity) until the sauce is thick and butterscotch colour.

Beat in remaining ingredients and finish sauce as above.

Brandy Butter

Traditionally served with hot Christmas pudding, mince pies, or other Christmas desserts. Serve chilled so that the butter melts onto the pudding. It can be made in advance and kept overnight in the fridge, or frozen until needed.

Serves 4-6   Preparation time: 10 minutes – take butter from fridge and leave to soften before use

100g/4 oz butter – preferably unsalted
100g/4 oz soft brown sugar or caster sugar
2 tbsp brandy

Put butter and chosen sugar in a bowl or mixer, and beat until pale, soft and creamy. Beat in brandy a little at a time.

Pile into a small serving dish, cover with plastic film and chill in fridge until needed.

Rum or Whisky Butter

Use 2 tbsp of chosen spirit instead of brandy.

Sherry Butter

Use caster sugar and dry or cream sherry instead of brandy.

Orange Butter

A refreshingly flavoured sauce, suitable for all the family.

100g/4 oz unsalted butter
100g/4 oz sieved icing sugar
Grated rind and juice of 1-2 dessert oranges

Beat butter until soft, then gradually beat in icing sugar. Beat in orange rind and enough juice to make a stiff sauce, then spoon into a serving dish, cover and chill until needed.

Raspberry Satin Sauce

A smooth melba sauce to pour over summer fruits, ice cream, hot sponge puddings or cold desserts.

Serves 4   *Preparation time: 10 minutes*

225g/8 oz raspberries – fresh, frozen and defrosted, or canned
75-100g/3-4 oz sieved icing sugar

Wash fresh raspberries and drain in a colander.

Put raspberries (fresh washed, frozen or canned with juice) into a liquidizer or blender, and mix for a few moments.

Pour into a nylon sieve and push fruit through the mesh into a bowl, making a beautiful, smooth, deep red purée.

Sweeten to taste with sieved icing sugar.

Keep in fridge until ready to use.

Sauce made from fresh or canned raspberries may be put into a lidded plastic container and frozen until needed.

Strawberry Melba Sauce

Not a traditional melba sauce, but useful to make when strawberries are cheap or you have some ripe fruit that needs using up. Pour over ice cream, fruit or puddings.

225g/8 oz ripe strawberries
1 tsp lemon juice
1-2 tbsp sieved icing sugar to taste

Wash and hull strawberries, put in blender or liquidizer and mix for a moment, then put purée through a nylon sieve.

Mix in lemon juice and sweeten to taste with icing sugar.

Store in fridge until ready to use.

Warm Coconut Sauce

A lovely sauce to serve over ice cream, puddings or cake.

Serves 6-8   *Preparation time: 15 minutes*

405g can sweetened condensed milk
50g/2 oz butter
2 egg yolks
50g/2 oz desiccated coconut
50g/2 oz chopped nuts – cashew, pecan or mixed nuts
½ tsp vanilla essence

Put condensed milk, butter and well beaten egg yolks into a heavy-based pan over a very low heat and cook gently for about 10 minutes, stirring all the time, until sauce thickens.

Mix in coconut, chopped nuts and vanilla essence, and use at once, or store in fridge and reheat gently before serving.

Pineapple Sauce

A warm sauce, delicious with pineapple sponge puddings.

Serves 4-6   *Preparation time: 10 minutes*

Small 200g can crushed pineapple
300ml/½ pint pineapple juice – use a carton
2 tsp cornflour or arrowroot
1-2 tsp sugar to taste – optional

Put crushed pineapple and pineapple juice into a pan. Put cornflour or arrowroot into a small basin and mix to a runny paste with 2-3 teaspoons of the pineapple juice from the pan.

Pour cornflour or arrowroot mixture into the sauce, then cook over a gentle heat, stirring all the time until sauce thickens.

Sweeten to taste, if needed. Serve at once, or store in fridge and reheat before serving.

Store Cupboard Sauces

Quickly prepared sauces, using everyday ingredients from the fridge or cupboard. Serve your choice of sauce with sponge or suet puds, pies or fruit fritters – delicious!

Each recipe serves 4-6 and takes about 5 minutes to prepare

Jam or Marmalade Sauce

4 heaped tbsp jam or marmalade
1 tbsp granulated sugar
150ml/¼ pint water
Grated rind and juice of 1 lemon
1 tsp cornflour

Put jam or marmalade, sugar, water and lemon rind into a small, heavy-based pan.

Mix cornflour to a runny paste with lemon juice, and stir into sauce mixture.

Bring sauce to the boil over moderate heat and cook for 2-3 minutes until sauce thickens, stirring with a wooden spoon. Pour sauce over pudding or serve separately in a jug.

Sticky Syrup Sauce

Make as Jam Sauce, using golden syrup instead of jam, and omitting the sugar, as the syrup is sweet enough on its own.

Charlbury Lemon Sauce

A 'meals on wheels' favourite made by Margaret the Chef.

Make as Jam Sauce, using 4 heaped tbsp lemon curd instead of jam, and the rind and juice of two lemons.

When sauce has thickened, sweeten to taste with extra sugar if liked.

Crème Anglaise

This recipe will please my friend Kim, who shocked her colleague Chris by confessing that she didn't really like puddings and only ate the custard! This custard is rich and delicious, and is certainly good enough to eat on its own!

Serves 4   *Preparation time: 10 minutes*

3 egg yolks
1 tsp cornflour
1 tbsp caster sugar
¼ tsp vanilla essence
300ml/½ pint whipping cream

Put egg yolks in a basin and whisk until runny. Beat in cornflour, caster sugar and vanilla essence.

Heat chosen cream in a heavy-based pan until almost boiling, then whisk into egg mixture, beating all the time.

Pour sauce back into saucepan, and cook over a very low heat, whisking all the time, until custard thickens. Remove from heat, and serve hot or cold.

For a thicker custard, use double cream.

Special Custard

A creamy rich custard using custard powder.

Serves 4-6   *Preparation time: 10 minutes*

2 tbsp or 1 packet custard powder
1-2 tbsp granulated sugar – to taste
600ml/1 pint double, whipping, single cream or a mix of milk and cream

Make custard according to instructions on the carton or packet, either in a heavy-based saucepan or a microwave – the richer the cream chosen, the thicker the custard will be. Serve hot or cold.

Chantilly Crème

A fluffy whipped cream, made lighter and less rich by the addition of the stiffly whipped egg white.

NB These Chantilly crèmes contain raw egg and should not be given to young children, pregnant women or elderly people.

Serves 4-6   *Preparation time: 10 minutes*

150ml/¼ pint double cream
2 tsp caster sugar
Few drops vanilla essence
1 egg white

Put cream, sugar and vanilla essence into a bowl or mixer and beat until creamy and thick but not solid.

Put egg white in another bowl and beat until stiff.

Fold egg white into thick cream, using a metal spoon.

Pile into a serving bowl and leave in fridge until needed.

Almond Chantilly Crème

This light, almond-flavoured crème is delicious served with mincemeat tarts and other Christmassy desserts.

Make as above, but omit the vanilla essence, and add ¼ teaspoon of almond essence with the sugar.

Chocolate Chantilly Crème

Make as above, but use 2 tsp sweetened drinking chocolate instead of caster sugar and omit vanilla essence.

Crème Patisserie

The most delicious cream to use as a filling with fruit in a tarte or flan, or to serve as a special alternative to whipped cream or custard.

Serves 4, or fills a 20cm/8 in tarte or flan with fruit on top

Preparation time: 15 minutes

3 egg yolks
½ tsp vanilla essence
75g/3 oz caster sugar
1 heaped tbsp plain flour
300ml/½ pint milk – preferably full cream
Small knob unsalted butter
The crème can be flavoured with 1-2 tsp lemon or orange
**   juice, brandy, rum, cream liqueur or sherry**

Put egg yolks, vanilla essence and sugar into a bowl and whisk until very thick and creamy.

Whisk in flour a little at a time, and then gradually add the milk, whisking slowly to make a smooth sauce.

Rinse a small, heavy-based saucepan with cold water (to stop sauce sticking), pour mixture into pan and bring to the boil over a moderate heat, stirring or whisking gently all the time.

When mixture boils, lower heat at once and simmer gently for 2-3 minutes, still whisking as the crème thickens.

Remove pan from heat, beat in butter and add any extra flavouring to taste – I think it's gorgeous just plain vanilla!

Pour sauce into a clean basin, sprinkle a scant teaspoonful of caster sugar over the top to prevent a skin forming, and leave to cool.

Cover with a lid or plastic film, and store crème in fridge until ready to use.

Mary's American Vanilla Cookies

The cookies are quick to make and super served with fruit desserts, custards, chocolate mousse or ice creams; or just enjoy them on their own when no one's looking – like my son Chris when his wife Mary has been busy baking!

Makes about 36-40 cookies, according to size
Preparation & cooking time: 35-45 minutes

225g/8 oz butter (room temperature) or soft margarine
75g/3 oz granulated sugar
175g/6 oz muscavado sugar
2 eggs
1 tsp vanilla essence
250g/9 oz plain flour
1 tsp bicarbonate soda

Heat oven at 190°C/375°F/fan oven170°C/gas 5-6, and grease several baking sheets – the cookies spread as they bake.

Put butter or margarine with white and brown sugar in a bowl, mixer or processor, and beat until fluffy and creamy. Mix eggs and vanilla essence together, and beat into butter mixture a little at a time. Sieve flour and bicarbonate, and stir into the mixture.

Drop in small round teaspoonfuls onto the greased baking sheets, allowing plenty of room for cookies to flatten and spread as they cook. Bake for 8-10 minutes, until cookies are just a pale brown – do not overcook, as the centres should be moist and chewy.

Remove from oven, allow to cool for a few moments, then carefully lift onto a wire cooling tray and leave to go cold.

Store in an airtight container until needed.

Nutty Lemon Cookies

Omit vanilla, add grated rind of 2 lemons with the eggs. Add 100g/4 oz chopped mixed nuts with the flour.

Chocolate Chip Cookies

Add 250g/8 oz plain chocolate chips with the flour.

INDEX

'He is my so
get to know
he's like…'

'Yes, of course.'

'I know you don't want me here…'

'Not "want",' she corrected hastily. 'Can't. Can't,' she repeated. 'I *told* you…'

'Yes. Suppose I don't ever get it back, Gellis?'

'Don't do this.'

'I must. *Have* to. He's my son. Let me stay…get to know him. I've lost my memory, my life. Don't let me lose my son too… You will allow me to stay, Gellis?'

She gave a helpless nod…but she wasn't really listening to what he asked. She was aware only of his touch, and the knowledge that he was staying. The alarming knowledge that they would be sharing the house. A very small house.

'There's only one bedroom,' she blurted out thickly.

Emma Richmond was born during the war in north Kent. She says, 'Amiable and disorganised, I'm married with three daughters, all of whom have fled the nest—probably out of exasperation! The dog stayed, reluctantly. I'm an avid reader, a compulsive writer and a besotted new granny.'

What others have said about Emma Richmond:

'Emma Richmond's stories have it all—humour, emotion and wonderful, memorable characters.'
Day Leclaire, author of *THE SECRET BABY* and the *FAIRYTALE WEDDINGS* trilogy.

Of **THE BACHELOR CHASE**
'Emma Richmond entertains with wit and strong emotional intensity.'
Romantic Times

Of **MORE THAN A DREAM**
'…emotionally charged, thought-provoking book. A true love story.'
Romantic Times

'…unique romance. Richmond has a magic way of making you wait breathlessly for the next hurdle and its tragic outcome or glorious victory.'
Affaire de Coeur

Emma Richmond has sold over seven million books worldwide!

Recent titles by the same author:

BEHAVING BADLY!
SECRET WEDDING

A HUSBAND
FOR CHRISTMAS

BY
EMMA RICHMOND

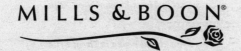

MILLS & BOON®

*First published in Great Britain 1997
Harlequin Mills & Boon Limited,
Eton House, 18-24 Paradise Road, Richmond, Surrey TW9 1SR*

© Emma Richmond 1997

ISBN 0 263 80494 1

*Set in Times Roman 11 on 12 pt.
02-9712-45790 C1*

*Printed and bound in Great Britain
by Mackays of Chatham PLC, Chatham*

CHAPTER ONE

THICK dark hair hung to her waist in a loosely woven plait, big brown eyes surveyed the world without interest. Beautiful, introspective, sad. Oblivious of the Christmas jingle that played endlessly over the loudspeaker, the noisy chatter, Gellis stared inward, wrapped up in her own thoughts. The opening of the café door brought momentary awareness—and then shock.

Déjà vu—except it wasn't. Unable to tear her eyes away, rigid with disbelief, *uncomprehending*, she stared at the tall, dark-haired man as he took the table next to her own. Hard and tough, fit. Ruthless. He had a badger stripe at his left temple, but it *was* Sébastien. Hazel eyes with those startling flecks of green stared dismissively round—until they found Gellis. And then they stopped. With a leisurely, almost insulting examination of her exquisite face, he gave a cynical smile of appreciation.

She didn't smile back. *Couldn't* smile back. There was no warmth in that glance, no humour. It *was* Sébastien, but not the Sébastien she had known. Loved. That Sébastien's eyes had been filled with laughter, and he had looked what he was—what she had thought he was, she corrected with bitter anguish—a humorous and honest man. And his dark hair had had no streak of white.

Eighteen months ago, in another café, another place, they had exchanged glances—and love had

5

been born. Not immediately, not instantly, but it had been born. And consummated.

Frozen in place, she continued to stare—and he raised one eyebrow in mocking question.

She was unable to respond, unable to do *anything* but sit there like a fool. He frowned, asked harshly, 'You know me?' And when she didn't answer, merely continued to stare at him in shock, he reached out, grabbed her forearm, hard. 'I asked if you knew me!' he gritted.

A catch in her throat, a little sound of distress; she lurched to her feet, prepared to flee.

'Sit down,' he grated. 'Sit *down*!' With a ruthless disregard for any pain he might be causing her, he dragged her down to her seat. Face thrust forward, eyes hard, mouth a grim line, he asked with menacing softness, 'Who am I?'

'Don't do this,' she whispered. 'Oh, please don't do this.' And his frown deepened, making carved, ugly grooves between his brows.

'Do what? Do *what*?' he repeated savagely. '*Where* do you know me from? When?'

'You *know* when!' she cried.

'No, lady, I don't! So when?' he demanded urgently. 'More than four months ago?'

Throat tight, the most awful ache in her chest, eyes fixed on his in disbelief and pain, she gave a jerky nod, and he let out a shuddering sigh, briefly closed his eyes.

'And my name is?'

'What?' she asked in a frightened little whisper.

'What's my name? What's my *name*, dammit?'

'Sébastien.'

'Sébastien,' he echoed, and his free hand curled

into a tight fist. 'Sébastien what? Sébastien *what*?' he repeated menacingly when she didn't answer.'

'Fourcard.'

'French?'

'Yes. *Yes!*' she shouted in distress.

'From?'

'Collioure.' And he closed his eyes again, let out a breath that seemed to Gellis as though it had been held for a very long time.

'Sébastien Fourcard,' he repeated quietly. 'From Collioure. *Mon Dieu.* At last.' Opening his eyes, he stared at her. 'And you are?'

'Gellis.'

'Gellis,' he echoed flatly.

'You're hurting me,' she asserted.

Staring at her arm as though quite unaware that he had been holding it in an iron fist, he hastily released it. '*Pardon.* And we were, what? Friends? Lovers?'

Snatching her eyes away, she too stared at her arm, watched the white imprint of his fingers slowly turn red. Oh, dear God. Oh, dear, dear God. How could he not remember? Of all the scenarios she had envisaged over the past four months, that had not been one of them. She had conjured up excuse after excuse for his behaviour, even blamed herself—but had not dreamed that he wouldn't remember her. Or himself. Or *himself*? Snapping her eyes back to his, she opened her mouth, closed it. And he gave a cruel smile.

'Yes,' he agreed harshly. Leaning back in his chair, eyes still fixed unwaveringly on her face, he explained flatly, 'I have no memory of events, people, places prior to August this year.' Touching the white stripe of hair, as though it was something he did rather a lot, he added mockingly, 'And until I sat at this table a few minutes ago I did not even know my own name So, acquaintances, friends—or lovers?'

Numb, barely able to comprehend, she just stared He'd lost his *memory*?

'Lovers,' he guessed. 'Only a lover could look that reproachful. What did I do? Run out on you?'

And she didn't think she could bear it. Not his mockery, not his harshness, nor the consequences if she told him what else he was responsible for. Shoving back her chair, she tried to escape. He grabbed her arm, forced her back down. Oblivious of the stares, the whispers, he repeated, 'What did I do?'

'Nothing,' she denied hollowly. 'Nothing at all.' And because she didn't want to talk about what he had done—what it had done to her—because she didn't even think she believed this was happening, she asked numbly, 'How did it happen? An accident?'

'Definitely lovers,' he murmured with a twisted smile. 'Otherwise you wouldn't have changed the subject, would you? Well, at least I had good taste. Yes,' he finally agreed, 'it was an accident.'

'Where?'

'South America.'

'South *America*?' Snatched out of her lethargy, she demanded blankly. 'What were you doing in South America?'

He gave a mocking smile.

'Oh,' she murmured foolishly. 'You don't remember.'

'No. So, when did we last meet? And where?'

Thinking back over the last dreadful months, she closed her eyes in pained defeat. 'August,' she stated softly. 'In France.'

'And how long were we—lovers?'

Lovers? Yes, they had been lovers. Looking down, the ache in her heart enormous, she whispered, 'Over a year.'

'And then I left you? Or did you leave me?' he asked mockingly.

Eyes bleak, she stared blindly at the scarred wooden table. What to say? That he had broken her heart? Destroyed her faith in human nature? And she needed to know *why*? And until she knew that... 'It was mutual,' she finally murmured.

With a sceptical little smile, he shrugged. 'But you know what I did? Where I lived? All about me?'

'Yes.' Or thought she had.

He didn't say anything more for a while, but she could feel him watching her, and she wanted to get up, run away, go and think about this in private. Shaken to the roots of her being by this unexpected encounter, she didn't know what to say, feel, think.

Because it hadn't been mutual. He'd said he was going away for a few days, some business venture he wanted to investigate—and he hadn't come back. He had sent a terse little note. And for the past four months every moment that hadn't been taken up with other things had been spent trying to find him. Trying to find out why. And now he was here, and she didn't know what to do.

Looking up at him at long last, her dark brown eyes full of distress, she stared at him in utter helplessness.

'Mutual for the sake of pride?' he asked quietly. 'Yes, I can see that it was. I hurt you, didn't I?'

An understatement, she thought bitterly, and perspicacity she could have done without. But, yes, he had hurt her. Hurt her so badly she had just wanted to die.

Those first few weeks had been a waking nightmare. Trying to find him, feeling sick and anxious, frightened—but it had been as though he had vanished into thin air. His bank wouldn't tell her if he had drawn any money from his account. Airlines and boats did not have his name on their lists, or, if they did, wouldn't admit it. She'd checked hospitals, the police, even funeral directors.

And as the weeks, and then months, had passed with no news hurt and despair had turned to hatred. Or so she had tried to tell herself. But there had always been that hope that one day she would find out the truth. Find out why he had done what he had. That it was all some sort of ghastly mistake. And now here he was, a harsh-faced stranger with no memory of her at all.

'Yes,' she finally admitted, 'you hurt me very badly.' And it was he who looked away. Stared through the window into the busy high street.

'What was I like?'

'Kind.' she murmured sadly. And loving and exciting, with an accent to curl her toes. But even the accent was harsher now. Grating. And she'd expected to hate him if ever she saw him again. And she somehow—couldn't.

'Kind,' he scoffed bitterly. 'Dear God, I don't feel as though I've ever been kind in my life. You don't only lose your memory, you lose the feelings that went with it.'

'You don't remember anything?'

'No.' Flicking his eyes back to hers, he gave a mocking smile. 'What did I do when you knew me? Was I gainfully employed, as they say?'

'No. You were taking time off, looking round for

something to do,' she added quietly. 'You'd had a string of restaurants you'd sold just before we met.'

'Which was?'

She gave a sad little smile. 'Eighteen months ago.'

'Which means we parted just before I went to South America.'

'Yes.'

'But you didn't know I was going? Or why?'

'No.'

'So if I didn't spend the money from the sale of the restaurants in South America I presumably still have some.'

'Yes.'

'Relatives?'

Relatives? She felt a little bubble of hysteria rise up in her throat. Relatives? Oh, yes, you have relatives, Sébastien. You have a wife and a son. A son that you delivered and then abandoned. But she couldn't tell him that, could she? Because he didn't remember. And if she did tell him he might want to come—home. So until she knew why he had left…

Staring at him, her gentle face harder, firmer, she shook her head. 'No. Not to my knowledge.' Just close friends, intimate friends—like Nathalie, she thought bitterly. Nathalie, who had completed the horror that Sébastien had started. But he had presumably also forgotten Nathalie, and she wasn't about to reintroduce her.

'What's wrong?'

'Nothing,' she denied quickly. Making an effort, trying to think what she should do, she asked instead, 'What are you doing in Portsmouth?'

'Disembarking. I was a deck hand on the *Pilbeam*. Cargo ship.'

'Oh. You remembered you liked the sea?'

'No—did I?'

'Yes, you used to go out sailing quite a lot.'

A rather bleak expression in his eyes, he gave a brief laugh. 'It was—expedient. The easiest way out of South America. No papers, no money; someone took me on as a deck hand. And, in between trying to find out who I was, deck hand I've been ever since.'

'Why did you have no papers or money?'

'Because someone presumably "lifted" them whilst I was unconscious after the accident.'

'Car?'

'Truck.'

'Then how have you managed since?' She frowned. 'With no papers…'

He reached into his pocket, tossed a passport down in front of her.

Taking it in a hand that still shook, she opened it. It was his picture, but the name was William Blake.

'You didn't know you were French?'

'Yes—or assumed, anyway. I *think* in French,' he explained. 'But it wouldn't have mattered if I was Chinese. Beggars can't be choosers, can they?'

'No,' she agreed, and didn't know how she could sit here and talk about incidentals with a man who had betrayed her, disappeared from her life, and had now come back. Still feeling numb, disbelieving, she asked foolishly, 'Is it…?'

'Forged? What do you think?'

'But surely the authorities could have helped you?'

'Could they?'

'Yes! In South America…'

He shrugged. 'They did their best. But with no paper, no memory, no knowledge of what I was doing there, no missing persons reported...' he added bitterly as he remembered those frustrating, fruitless days.

'But when you got out,' she persisted weakly. 'Surely the French authorities would have helped?'

'Why? I couldn't prove I was French. According to them, I was just another illegal immigrant. And suppose I wasn't French but French Canadian? From somewhere else that speaks French? You think I didn't try?'

Feeling sad and lost, unprepared for this, Gellis asked emptily, 'So it was just coincidence that you came to Portsmouth?'

'Not entirely. Do you live here?'

Hesitating for a moment, she tried to think rationally, sensibly. But her mind was a whirl of conjecture, speculation, worry, and so she nodded, because it seemed best not to tell him the truth.

'So I would have known the town? Would have been here?'

'Yes.'

He nodded thoughtfully. 'Then I was right. I've been here several times, looking, waiting, hoping. When I was found after the accident I was wearing a brown leather belt. Stamped on the inside was the name and address of a shop in Portsmouth. Presumably where it was made and bought. Unfortunately, the shop has since closed down.'

'Yes,' she agreed.

'You know it?'

She nodded.

'You bought it for me?'

'No,' she denied quietly. 'My mother. She bought

it for you for Christmas.' And this Christmas, in a
few weeks' time, there would be no presents for
Sébastien. Not from her parents. Not from herself. No
presents from Sébastien to his—family. With a hard,
painful ache inside, she asked listlessly, 'Will it come
back? Your memory?'

'Who knows?' he shrugged.

'You've seen doctors?'

'Yes,' he agreed mockingly.

'What will you do now?'

'Go to France. With you.'

Shocked, utterly panicked, she just stared at him. 'I
can't go to France!'

'Why not?'

'Because I can't!' Couldn't go anywhere with this
man! And you couldn't go back, could you? Yet she
had loved him. No—she had loved the man he had
been. And getting to know him again would be—dangerous. Hardening her heart and her mind, she shook
her head. 'No. I have a new life now. I'm sorry
you've lost your memory, I'm sorry you've been hurt.
I'll give you the addresses I know in France that
might help, but—'

'No,' he put in softly.

'What?'

'No,' he repeated. 'You are the only person I've
found in four months who knew me. The only person
who can tell me what I was like. Are there others in
Collioure who would know me?'

'Yes, you have a rented apartment there.'

'Have?' he frowned.

'Yes. The bank automatically pays the rent each
month. At least, I assume they're still doing so.'

'And we lived there together?'

'Yes.'

'As lovers?'

'Yes!' she agreed tightly.

'And then I, what? Got bored with you? Met someone else?'

Yes! her mind screamed. You met Nathalie. Nathalie who was beautiful and blonde and French. 'You went out one day,' she stated flatly, 'and didn't come back.'

'And you didn't look for me?' he asked with that hatefully mocking smile.

Slamming to her feet, she glared down at him. 'Yes, I looked for you! Looked and looked and looked! And even though—' Biting off what she had been going to say, she grabbed up her bag and ran away.

Wrenching open the café door, she hurried out onto the crowded pavement. She was shaking. Badly. Why? she wondered in despair. Why? And it hurt. Dear God, how it hurt. But she had survived four months without him, and so she could survive more. And, lost memory or no, there was no getting away from what he had done.

Shutting off her mind, her emotions, she strode quickly down the street, turned off towards where her car was parked—and he grabbed her arm.

'Don't touch me!' she gritted. 'Don't ever touch me!'

Swinging round, she glared at him. She wasn't a vengeful girl, or malicious, but she'd been through too much. Had suppressed the pain and anger, the despair, but now there was a focus for it. Someone to blame. 'Just don't touch me,' she repeated heavily.

Shaking, she turned away, and he stopped her, held her firm.

'I said…'

'I know.' Gently turning her, he leaned her against the wall. Examined her exquisite face. The defiance in her eyes. 'But do you have any idea what it's like not to know? To have no memories of self?'

Looking away, she shook her head. 'I can imagine…'

'No, Gellis, you can't. No one can. Your life is shaped by what you are, how you live, loved. All I have is—nothing. A blank canvas. Your name echoes in an empty space. *All* names echo in an empty space.' Dropping his bag and jacket, he lifted his hands, held them out. 'Were my hands like this when you knew me?'

Still angry, still stiff, she stared at the calluses, the scars, then shook her head again.

'No. Four months,' he murmured, 'of hell. Rough work, rough places, even rougher people. But I survived. And now I have the chance to find out who I really am, and you're the only one who can help me. Two weeks, that's all I ask. Two weeks to help me find out who I am.'

Still staring at his hands, she gave a bitter smile. 'I can't.'

'Can't you? And if the positions were reversed, if you were the one with no memory, wouldn't you fight tooth and nail to make the one person who could help you help?'

'Yes,' she agreed helplessly. 'But I can't do it.' Looking up at him, she repeated flatly, 'I can't. Don't ask it of me.'

Touching his fingers gently to her cheek, he frowned when she flinched away. 'I hurt you so much?' he asked sombrely.

'Yes.'

'Then tell me. Make me understand.'

Tears filling her lovely eyes, she shook her head.

'Then look on it as a job,' he murmured with twisted mockery. 'I'll pay you.'

'I don't *want* paying,' she denied in distress. 'And don't mock me. Don't *ever* mock me! You don't have the right.'

'Obviously not. Ten days.'

'No!'

'Yes. How long will it take you to pack? An hour?'

'No! I can't go with you! Do you have any idea…? No,' she conceded wearily, 'of course you don't. But take my word for it, Sébastien, I can't go with you.'

'*Won't* go with me,' he corrected her grimly.

'Yes. Won't go with you.' And if he had remembered what he had done to her he would never have asked. Or would he?

Leaning towards her, hands flat on the wall behind her, his voice low, he stated urgently, 'This is my *life*, Gellis! It's not some Women's Institute meeting where we're discussing the price of jam! I've had four lost months. Not days, not weeks, but months! And, without you, I might lose years. Whatever I did, I don't remember; I wish to God I did! I'm sorry if I hurt you! Sorry if I caused you pain, but you're my only *hope*, Gellis.'

'I can't,' she denied desperately.

'You can! For God's sake, I'm not asking you to go to the ends of the earth! Just across the damned Channel. I need to *know*, Gellis! Can't you understand that? I need to *know*.'

So do I, she thought bleakly. So do I.

'Please!'

And this was not a man who begged.

'Please,' he repeated.

Holding his eyes for endless moments, she finally slumped, looked down, shuddered. Oh, God. It was still there—the feeling, the want, the need—and if she went with him…

And if she didn't? If she ran away now, spent the rest of her life hiding, she would never find out the truth. And she did need to know the truth. Needed to know why he had done what he had. But she didn't know if she could bear to be in his company—not because of what he had done, but because of the way he could make her feel.

Because she so desperately wanted him back. After all that had happened, she still wanted him. At first, in the café, when he had seemed so unfamiliar, so harsh and grating, there had been only shock, disbelief, panic. But now…

'Just take me there,' he urged. 'Show me where we lived.'

'The people there will show you,' she argued desperately.

'I don't know the people there.'

Closing her eyes in defeat, she wondered if it was a nightmare that would ever end. And he was too close, made her feel stifled, and she had to keep shutting her mind off in an effort not to think, feel—because she wanted to be held, comforted… Clenching her hands tight, she shook her head.

'Just to Collioure, and then you can come back home,' he encouraged.

Home, she thought bleakly. Without him, it wasn't a home at all. And the only way to get rid of him was to agree, wasn't it? Otherwise he would stand here for

ever, and for ever, persuading, undermining her resolution... 'I can't go for long,' she muttered. And she
couldn't look at him. Not look into those beautiful
eyes. Treacherous eyes. Eyes that had lied. As hers
would be lying if she looked at him.

'Thank you.'

'I'll meet you back here tomorrow.'

And he laughed. A harsh, grating sound that sent a
shiver through her.

'Do I look like a fool, Gellis?' he asked disparag-
ingly. 'We go today.'

'*Today?* No! I can't go today!' She panicked.
Glancing at her watch, glancing at *anything* in order
not to have to look at him, she murmured stupidly,
'It's already gone eleven.'

'So? The sooner we go, the sooner you can return.'

Well, it didn't matter what she said, did it? Because
she wasn't intending to actually *go*! 'All right. I'll
meet you back here in an hour.'

'No.'

'What?'

'I said, no. You really think I believe you will come
back? No, Gellis, I will come with you.'

'No!'

And he smiled. Like a wolf. 'Yes.'

Glancing frantically round, she found to her despair
and astonishment that the pavement was empty.

'Intending to scream?' he asked softly and really
rather menacingly.

Could she? Dared she?

His smile widened, showed even white teeth—teeth
she had touched with her tongue—and she began to
feel slightly sick. 'You're English,' he whispered in
hateful amusement. 'And the English don't scream,

do they? Don't like to attract attention to themselves. Give in gracefully, Gellis.'

And that angered her—his mockery, his assumption. 'No.' Straightening her back, she forced one of his arms away. 'No,' she repeated.

His smile dying, he searched her defiant eyes. 'What did I do?' he asked sombrely. 'In God's name, what did I *do*?'

CHAPTER TWO

'You left!' Gellis shouted. 'Hurt me. Sent a terse little note to say you wouldn't be back!'

Sébastien frowned. 'No explanation? No reason?'

'No.'

'And so you don't know why?'

'No.'

'But you would like to, wouldn't you? That's human nature—to want to know why. If you come with me, you might find out.'

Yes, she might find out. And if it was something she didn't want to hear? At least she would *know*. Not be forever speculating. There was the future to think of. A need to put it all behind her.

Eyes too big in her white face, she slowly raised her lashes, forced herself to look at him. *Really* look at him. A hard face, but so very attractive. But no longer her husband's face. Go with him? See their friends again? Be in his company? She didn't know if she was tough enough.

'You're wavering,' he said quietly.

'Am I?' she asked stonily. 'All right,' she decided. 'I'll come with you. But I can't go for long—no more than a few days.' No she couldn't go for long.

'Vengeance is mine, saith the Lord?' he queried soberly.

'What? No. I don't want vengeance. Just to know the truth.'

'As do I. Thank you,' he added quietly. Straight-

21

ening, he gave her an odd smile—quirky, a little bit wry. 'Which way?'

Keeping her heart hard, her mind still, she pointed to their right.

He nodded. Hooking up his duffel bag and sailing jacket, he waited for her to lead the way.

'Which is the nearest airport?'

'Airport?' she queried absently.

'Yes, Gellis, airport.'

She shook her head. 'We aren't flying.'

'Aren't we?' he mocked softly.

'No. We'll go by car.'

'That will take two days.'

'I don't care. I'm not flying.'

'Why not?'

'Because I don't *like* to!' she gritted.

'Fair enough.'

Surprised by his easy acceptance, she gave a bitter smile. This was madness.

He halted, swung her to face him, stared down into her expressionless face, then registered the pain in her lovely eyes. Big and brown and lost. Like a doe. With a muffled sigh, he turned to walk on. 'Where are we going?'

'To my car.'

He nodded. 'You have a current passport?'

'Yes.'

He smiled. 'Didn't even think of lying, Gellis?'

'Would it have done me any good?'

He shook his head. 'If I had to take your house apart to find your birth certificate, I would have done so.'

'And then dragged me up to town to get a new one.'

'Yes. However long it took.'

She believed him. Utterly.

'We can get a ferry from here?'

'We'll go on Le Shuttle.'

He gave another odd smile. 'Don't like sailing either?'

'No,' she replied stonily.

'How did you manage before it was built?'

'With difficulty. My car's over there.'

Glancing at the gleaming red sports car, he gave a silent whistle, looked at her with new interest. He'd assumed she'd have a sedate hatchback.

'You bought it for me,' she stated shortly as she opened the boot for him to put his belongings inside. After the birth of their son.

'Generous of me.'

'Yes.' Climbing behind the wheel, she watched without amusement as he folded his considerable length in beside her. His head brushed the roof.

'There's a lever on your right to lower the seat.' She had a moment's compunction that on the long drive to the south of France he was going to be extremely uncomfortable, then dismissed it. She hadn't asked for this. But it was something she had to do, wasn't it? *Wasn't* it?

There was sexual awareness as there had been that first time they'd met, but no feeling of excitement or warmth. Just despair. And pain. And perhaps fear. She was probably still in shock. And when she came out of it? The panic returning, she slowed, whispered, 'I can't do this.'

'Yes, you can,' he argued with flat insistence. 'It's my life, Gellis.'

'I know.' But it was hers too. And, seemingly without any choice in the matter, she drove the short distance to her parents' house.

She tried to imagine it from his point of view. Tried to imagine having no memory. And couldn't. And if Nathalie hadn't come to see her after she'd received that note... But she *had* come, and so the matter was academic. He'd cheated. Deliberately lied. And if he had been the same man she'd loved... But he wasn't. He was a grim-faced stranger. Hard and tough. Dangerous. But they both needed to find out the truth, didn't they?

She didn't park directly outside the house but a few doors along, and, glancing at him worriedly, said quietly, 'I'll be as quick as I can. You'll stay here?'

He nodded.

'Give me your word.'

He looked at her, his eyes hard and direct. 'You have it.'

'Thank you.' Feeling sick and shaky, disbelieving, she climbed out, and he watched her walk across the road. Watched the hypnotic sway of the long, loosely woven plait that hung to her waist. The seductive movement of her hips. An exceptionally beautiful woman. Tall and slender, graceful. The sort of woman people looked at twice because she was—different. With a long neck, narrow hands and feet, she walked as though she was special. Someone he'd presumably loved.

And yet, when he looked into her face, he saw only bitterness, pain. A gentle girl, he suspected, who'd had to learn toughness the hard way. Because of him? What the hell had he done to make her look so distressed?

Shifting slightly, trying to find room for his long

legs, he gave a grim smile. He should have bought her a bigger car. Driving to France in this sardine can was going to be a real test of endurance. Well, he'd suffered worse and survived. And, at the end of it, would he finally remember?

She was back in just over an hour. Hair tied loosely back now, still damp from her shower, it hung like a brown, shiny curtain. Dressed in thick black cords and a white sweater, a black leather jacket slung round her shoulders, she carefully looked both ways before crossing the road. And he felt—attracted.

After putting her small suitcase in the boot, she climbed behind the wheel and handed him a map. 'Just in case,' she explained.

He nodded, glanced at the house, saw the curtain twitch and a woman with short dark hair peek out.

'Who's that?'

Glancing across, she murmured, 'My mother.'

'She lives with you?'

She shook her head. Switching on the ignition, she checked her mirrors then pulled away.

'Did I ever meet her?'

'Yes, and my father.'

'And?'

'They liked you.'

Turning his head, he stared at her profile. 'For four months there has been no one to ask questions of. I'm sorry if you think me—'

'No,' she broke in, distressed. 'But please try to see it from my point of view. I find this very hard. Ask what you need to.'

'Thank you. Was I ever here?'

'Yes,' she agreed quietly.

'They didn't mind us living together?'

Hesitating only briefly, she shook her head.

Still watching her, he asked, 'Were you in love with me, Gellis?'

A swift, sharp pain in her heart, she gave a bitter smile. 'Yes.' So much. More than life.

'But I left you.'

'Yes.'

'We didn't have a row? Anything like that?'

'No.'

'And I didn't tell you I was going to South America?'

'No.'

He was silent for a moment, and then he asked quietly, 'Were we happy, Gellis?'

With another bitter smile, she murmured, 'I thought so, yes.' She'd thought it was the love story to end all love stories. And perhaps it had been. But why, then, had he behaved as he had? She had made so many excuses for him in her mind, to her parents— tried to rationalise it, come to terms with it, and didn't suppose she ever would until she knew the truth. And he must have been an astonishingly good actor, mustn't he? Because, that last month, never by hint or deed had he ever intimated that he no longer loved her. Or their son. A son he'd delivered...

'Gellis?'

'I am going to die,' she stated confidently.

'Gellis!'

'If the next pain is as bad as the last, I am going to die.'

With a splutter of laughter, he climbed onto the bed beside her, held her in his arms. 'You aren't allowed to die,' he said softly.

Opening her eyes, she stared at him. *'Non?'*

'Non.'

'Well, if the ambulance doesn't get here soon, or the doctor—' Stiffening, she clutched at him, held her breath.

'Pant.'

'I don't want to pant,' she gasped. 'Oh, boy, I need to push.'

'Non,' he denied worriedly.

'Yes. Oh, God. Get some towels.'

'Towels?'

'Yes! *Vite!* Oh, Sébastien, quickly.'

Alarmed, he rolled to his feet, sprinted into the other room, grabbed a pile of towels and hurried back. He hovered, gave a ridiculous smile, asked foolishly, 'What do I do with them?'

'Oh, Sébastien!' she exclaimed on a weak laugh. 'Put them under me.'

'Right. Put them under you. Be calm,' he instructed himself. 'Be calm.' Gently raising her, he put several towels beneath her, closed his eyes, took a deep breath and smiled. A bit quirky, a bit lopsided, but a smile. 'I'm all right now.'

'Good.'

'I must deliver it, yes?'

'Yes.'

'Right.'

'Everything will be fine,' she gasped.

'Oui. And I remind myself that we *like* to do things differently. How fortunate I read the books.' He gave a shaky grin, then kissed her. 'Raise your knees.'

She raised them, eyes fixed trustingly on her husband.

Walking to the other end of the bed, he took another deep breath, and rested both hands heavily on the counterpane. *'Mon Dieu!'* he exclaimed weakly. 'I can see the head.'

'Is that good?'

'Certainly,' he said with more confidence than he was feeling. 'Now you must push. It will be all right, my darling.'

'I know,' she whispered. She gave him a shaky smile, gasped on another sudden pain, and he smiled, tried to sound confident. But there was anxiety in his eyes as there was in her own. A slight shake to his voice. 'That's fine; keep pushing. Gently, gently...'

Oh, God. 'It hurts.'

'I know.'

Gripping the bed-head with hands that trembled, she waited for the next pain, then pushed and, astonishingly, felt the head emerge.

Eyes wide, they stared at each other.

'Oh, *mon dieu!*' Gently supporting the head with his large hands, he instructed anxiously, 'One more.'

She pushed, and the baby slid out with no trouble at all.

'It's a baby,' he whispered in awe.

Supporting herself on her elbows, she peered down, gave a shaken laugh. 'What were you expecting? And is it all right?' she queried worriedly. 'Shouldn't it be crying or something?'

'Not if you're lucky,' a dry voice said from the doorway. 'And I suggest you wrap him up instead of marvelling at the commonplace.'

'Commonplace to you,' Sébastien said in soft awe. 'Not commonplace to me. I'm shaking.' Gently wrapping the baby in a towel, he halted, glanced at the doctor. 'The cord?'

'I will deal with the cord,' he said wryly. 'How are you, *madame*?' he asked as he deftly dealt with it and handed the baby to Sébastien.

'Fine,' Gellis said weakly.

'*Bien*. Another push, if you please, for the after-birth.'

Gellis obliged, and glanced at her husband as he cradled their new-born child in his arms. He looked— amazed. He glanced up, gave her an uncertain smile. 'I can't believe I did that.'

'I can,' she said softly as she held out her arms, gave him a smile that was soft with love. 'What is it? Boy or girl?' And he gave a comical blink.

'I forgot to look,' he murmured sheepishly. Lifting the towel, he smiled. 'A boy. Oh, Gellis, we have a son. So perfect,' he added almost reverently as he gently handed him over. Perching on the edge of the bed, he put his arm round her, lingeringly kissed her temple. 'I was frightened to death.'

'I was a bit nervous myself,' she confessed.

'Don't get comfortable,' the doctor warned Sébastien. 'I need you to get some hot water, and then to ring the nurse.' Dragging a piece of paper from his crumpled jacket, he handed it over. 'Tell her to get her pretty little *derrière* over here *tout de suite*.'

And when Gellis had been cleaned up, the baby checked and washed, she stared down at the little miracle in her arms and gave a contented sigh. 'He looks like you, don't you think?' she asked Sébastien softly as he came to sit beside her once more.

'Gellis! He looks like a—'

'Don't say it,' she warned.

'But he *does*!'

'He has your nose,' she said decisively.

He smiled, glanced at the doctor. 'The nurse will accompany us to the hospital? *When* the ambulance gets here,' he added pointedly.

'Hospital?' the doctor asked blankly. 'Why would you want to go to the hospital?'

'Because we've just had a baby?'

'A quite natural event, I assure you; women do it every day.'

'Not this woman!' Gellis said fervently.

'True.' Closing his bag with a snap, the doctor looked at her, smiled. 'And I could have wished you had not done it at four o'clock in the morning. However, an easy birth,' he informed her. 'No complications, no stitches, no tears. Do you *want* to go to the hospital?'

A bit bemused, she shook her head.

'Then I'll cancel the ambulance. And I'm quite sure that *monsieur* is capable of changing the bedding, doing all that needs to be done. Congratulations,' he added belatedly, then grinned. 'I will forgo the customary drink until a more reasonable time. I'm going back to my bed. The baby will do very well until the nurse arrives. Don't *fiddle* with him! Goodnight.'

Fiddle with him? A bit nonplussed, they stared at each other and burst out laughing. The baby gave a start, a little cry, and went back to sleep. Gazing down at him in wonder, neither of them really believing it, Sébastien gently touched the baby's cheek. 'I'm glad the ambulance was late,' he said softly. 'A special moment. I want to go and tell the world.'

'Start with my parents.'

'*Oui*,' he smiled, but he didn't immediately move.

She didn't know how long they sat there, just staring at their baby, but it seemed a long time, until

Sébastien stirred, gave a rueful smile. '*Monsieur* had better change the bedding.'

'Yes.' Reaching out her hand, smiling up at him with as much love and wonder in her face as his, she murmured gently, 'You were brilliant. Thank you. If you hadn't been here...'

Squeezing her fingers, then raising them to his mouth, he answered huskily, 'I will always be here. Thank you for our son. And now I will go and get the Moses basket, blankets, nappies...' With a laugh, a little shake of his head, he said wryly, 'And so it begins. A new life. Don't stop loving me, will you?'

Eyes filmed with tears, she shook her head.

'*Bien.*' Dropping a warm, lingering kiss on her mouth, he went to get all the necessary bits and pieces, and, when the nurse arrived, the baby was wrapped warmly in his cot, Gellis was asleep and Sébastien was watching her.

Don't stop loving me...

'Gellis. Gellis!'

With a little start, she blinked, turned to stare at him.

'The lights are green.'

'What?'

'The traffic lights. They're green.'

'Green? Oh, green.'

Feeling stupid, she quickly set the car in motion.

'What were you thinking about?' he asked quietly.

'Thinking? Oh, nothing,' she sighed. 'Nothing at all.' And wanted to weep. Had it all been acting? *All* of it? He'd been loving, kind, *tired*, because the baby had kept them awake at night—*and* during the day— but there had only ever been the normal difficulties associated with having a new baby. He hadn't been impatient, or irritable. Just wry.

He'd given no clue at all that he was intending to walk out on them both. Or had he not been intending to? Had it just been impulse? Because he'd had enough of domesticity? Certainly he didn't *look* like a domesticated animal. Glancing at him, at that strong profile, firm mouth, she sighed.

They didn't speak after that, but she was aware of the puzzled glances he gave her from time to time, the brooding intensity that emanated from him. And his bewilderment must be far greater than her own, mustn't it?

As she began picking up the signs for the terminal, she asked quietly, 'Have you seen the Shuttle? Used it?'

He shook his head. 'Not to my knowledge. Have you?'

'Mmm, a few months ago. I came—on holiday.' As she had kept coming on holiday to France in the small, useless hope that one day she might see him, find out the truth. 'It's brilliant.'

'Good. A new experience for me.'

'Yes,' she agreed helplessly. Halting at the booth, she purchased their tickets with her credit card, was advised on the times of the trains and wished a good journey.

'Do you want anything from the duty-free shop? Or shall we go straight to the train?'

When he didn't answer, merely frowned, she bit her lip, wondered if he actually had any money on him. 'I can lend you some money...' she began awkwardly. 'I mean...'

Glancing at her, he smiled. But it wasn't

Sébastien's smile. It wasn't gentle, just rather mockingly amused.

'I wasn't a deck hand for *free*. I got paid.'

'Oh.'

'But thank you anyway. I need to change it into francs. And I'll pay you back for the tickets when I come into my—''inheritance''.'

She nodded, drove round to the parking area beside the duty-free shops.

Queuing up for coffees, she watched him, watched other people watch him. He didn't look like a tourist. In fact, he looked like an extra from a movie. One about mercenaries, or piracy on the high seas. People gave him a wide berth. Probably wisely. There seemed very little of the old Sébastien left. This man was bigger, tougher. Harder.

'Yes?'

Swinging around, she quickly apologised. 'Sorry. Two coffees, please.'

After paying for them, she carried them over to a vacant table, and continued to watch Sébastien, tried so very hard to come to terms with this unreality. She didn't honestly know *how* she felt about him. In an odd sort of way, he fascinated her—perhaps because he was so very different from the man she had once known. Maybe she *was* still in shock.

As her mother had been—and then thoughtful, understanding. 'Go,' she had finally urged. 'If you don't, you will always wonder. Go, and be very careful.'

Yes, she would be careful.

He finished changing his money, put it carefully in his wallet and returned it to his back pocket. Looking round, he spotted her, began strolling towards her. Lithe, at ease, yet somehow alert. There was an arrogance about him, a look of indifference, dismissal, almost, of others. He looked as though he didn't give a damn about anybody, but cross him at your peril.

In clean jeans and a grey T-shirt, he wore them with the same ease he wore everything, whether it be dinner jacket or cords. Clothes didn't make Sébastien. Sébastien made the clothes. Or had.

'I got you a coffee,' she told him quietly. 'I didn't get anything to eat. I didn't know if you were hungry.'

He shook his head. Still standing, he picked up his coffee, tasted it, choked and replaced it on the table. 'How can anyone make something so good taste so bloody awful? Don't tell me you *like* it.'

'No,' she replied with a small smile. 'I think that has to be the worst coffee I have ever tasted in my life.'

'For sure,' he agreed fervently. 'I sometimes think the English make ruining coffee into an art form.'

'Probably. Shall we go?'

She had a moment's fear when they drove through the British and then the French frontier controls, but their passports were merely glanced at and then returned.

'You'd make a terrible smuggler,' he observed almost scathingly.

'How would you know? Been one, have you?'

'No,' he denied dismissively. 'And you're being waved on.'

Staring at the official, and then at the raised plates she was being asked to drive over, she bit her lip. 'I hope the car will go over them.'

'You didn't use this car when you came before?'

'Yes, but it only *just* cleared them. I should have checked the tyres, made sure they were fully inflated.'

Too late now. Easing cautiously forward, teeth clenched in anticipation of a crunch, ignoring the impatient official, she didn't breathe easily until she'd driven over the last one, and began following the signs towards the waiting area. 'They have them so that they know a car will have the necessary clearance on the train.'

'So I assumed.' Turning a mocking glance on her, he added softly, 'Loss of memory doesn't make me stupid.'

'I didn't say it did.'

'Was I stupid before?'

'No,' she denied stiffly. Neither were you so hatefully mocking.

They waited ten minutes, and then drove onto the train. The journey was smooth, silent, efficient, and, thirty-five minutes later, they were in France. Fortunately for her peace of mind, he hadn't stayed in the car with her. That would have been too much to bear. Whilst she was driving, concentrating, she could shut him from her mind. But, once she stopped, awareness stole back, cramped her muscles, filled her mind with memories.

'Impressive,' he murmured.

'Yes. I told you it was brilliant.'

'So you did.' Consulting the map, he ordered, 'Take the *autoroute*; it will be quicker.'

'I was intending to. I'll drive until it gets dark and then we'll find somewhere to stop for the night.'

'I'll need to stop for petrol…'

'And something to eat.'

'Yes.'

'You know the way? Which turn-offs to take?'

'Yes,' she agreed quietly. 'I know the way.' She'd

been this way so many times she could do it in her sleep. Looking for him. Always looking for him. And now she'd found him and didn't know him at all.

CHAPTER THREE

THEY spent the night in a small motel, in separate rooms, and, in the morning, they breakfasted together—as strangers. The last time they had driven this route, stopped overnight, there had been laughter and teasing. Love. Now there was just tension.

'Ready?'

Sébastien nodded.

'Over halfway,' Gellis added inanely as they made their way to the car.

'Yes.'

Climbing behind the wheel, she waited until he was settled, then pulled onto the road that would take them back to the *autoroute*.

Hours passed. Silent hours, tense hours, and the further they drove, the tenser it became. Stops for petrol or meals weren't much of a relief, and when they did speak conversation was stilted, unnatural. He, presumably, because he was nearing his goal and so much was riding on it. She because of the close proximity, the realisation of what she was actually doing.

And then there was only one last stop to make.

'Not much further,' she murmured as she stood beside him whilst he filled the car with petrol.

'No. I expect you're tired.'

'Yes, a bit.'

'Your French is very good.'

'Thank you. You taught me.'

37

'Did I? I wonder I had the patience,' he retorted a trifle bitterly.

Glancing at him, she saw that he was frowning, fingering the white stripe of hair.

'You cut your head in the accident?'

'Hmm? Oh, yes. Fourteen stitches,' he added absently. Removing the nozzle, he fitted it back in its slot, looked at her, then away.

With a little sigh, she walked to the booth to pay, and when she returned to the car she delayed a moment before climbing in, to stare round her. She loved France. Loved the people, the language. And now she was back. Briefly.

It was late afternoon when they reached the turn-off for Collioure, and she glanced at him. He'd been silent since they'd left the service station. Grimly so as he stared out at places he obviously didn't recognise, and she wondered what was going through his mind. Hope? Despair? It must be so frightening not to know who you were. What you had been. Done. And she was tired, worried about what the next few days would bring.

'Nearly there.'

'Are we?'

'Yes, just down the hill.' Slowing so that he could see the town spread out below them, the little red roofs, the sparkling sea, she glanced at his stern profile and saw that he was rubbing his fingers across his forehead. 'Does your head ache?'

'No.'

Her sigh muffled, she probed hesitantly, 'Does any of it seem familiar?'

'No.'

Probably best not to question him, prompt—but how could she not? How could she stay silent in the face of his pain? In the face of her own?

Feeling bewildered and inadequate, wishing now that she had not come, she turned into the little private car park that served the apartments. 'We have to walk from here,' she stated quietly.

He nodded, unlatched his door and got out. Collecting their bags from the boot, face grim, he hovered indecisively until Gellis had locked the car. 'This way. It's not far. I brought the key. I also rang the agent, told her we were coming, made sure it hadn't been relet.'

'Thank you.'

They didn't see anyone they knew as she led the way along the cobbled alley, for which she was thankful. She didn't think she could have coped with questions, curiosity. As the lane widened out to a small square, she felt a lump rise in her throat as she saw the planted tubs on everyone's wrought-iron balconies. No riot of colour at this time of year, but there were little shrubs, some white and mauve flowers. Someone had obviously replanted her own tubs— what had been her own tubs, she mentally corrected— because they were as pretty as everyone else's.

Halting outside their apartment, she tried to see it through his eyes, feel it through his confusion. Grey stone, leaded casement windows. Not large, not fancy, just—home.

Turning her head, she watched him, saw the complete absence of recognition. With a gesture that hurt her more than she could ever articulate, he unlatched the gate and stood like a stranger, the white streak at his left temple a flag of unfamiliarity. The hair across the scar tissue would never grow back dark. Always there would be that white streak as a reminder.

He turned to look at her, gave a wry smile, but his eyes were bleak. As bleak as her own. Taking out her key, she opened the door and led the way into a pretty apartment that suddenly felt cold, empty, unlived-in. Should she leave him? she wondered. Let him find his own way? Come to terms with it on his own?

'Would you prefer to be alone?' she asked quietly, and he shook his head.

'Then I'll make some coffee, shall I? The agent said she would stock up for us.'

'Yes,' he agreed absently, and pushed into the lounge.

Hands shaking, a cold feeling in the pit of her stomach, she went into the kitchen, felt the memories rush back and hastily banished them. She had to be hard. Distance herself.

A packet of coffee stood on the counter with sugar and a fresh loaf. The fridge had been switched on and inside were milk and butter, a few vegetables, fruit. With a deep sigh, she filled the percolator, switched it on, then opened the back door that led onto another little balcony. She saw that these plants too had been looked after. A cool wind blew off the sea, but it wasn't as cold as in England. Not as bleak. Only in her heart, she thought. That was bleak. Very bleak indeed.

And the last time they had driven from England to Collioure she had done exactly the same things. Switched on the percolator, come to check on her plants whilst he unloaded the luggage. And then he had come up behind her, slid his arms round her waist, held her against him, touched his mouth to her temple.

'Bed?' he had suggested with that devilish twinkle in his eyes. And then he had swept her up in his arms, carried her along to their room. His eyes had been laughing, his mouth curved in that wicked smile that had always been her undoing, and they'd lain on their wide bed and made love. So much passion there had been. Always so much passion. And now they were strangers, and she suddenly felt frightened. Frightened of a future that stretched bleak and empty.

Wrenching her mind away, she returned to the kitchen, got out their cups. Thick, heavy coffee-cups they'd bought in the market together. And she felt her eyes fill with tears for what might have been. What she had thought would be. Perhaps she should have worn his favourite outfit in the hope that it might jog his memory, she thought bitterly—should have worn his favourite perfume, left her dark hair loose, just as he'd liked it… And perhaps the eyes that had always been filled with laughter and love would flicker with memory.

And then what? An explanation for his behaviour? But supposing there wasn't an explanation? Supposing he just hadn't loved her any more? Or their son.

Leaving the coffee to percolate, she went to find him because she couldn't do anything else. The compulsion was coming back. The need. And that had always been the danger.

He was in their bedroom, wardrobe door open, staring at the few clothes hanging tidily inside. Standing quietly in the doorway, she watched him with an aching intensity, a hopeless yearning for it all to be different, all to be right. For him to turn, smile, say he remembered, that everything was all right. But he didn't—just continued to stare into the wardrobe with bitter hopelessness. Staring at him, at this bitter stranger, she tried to hate him. And couldn't.

He lifted out a jacket, tried it on, then gave a grim smile as it strained across his back. 'I've put on weight.'

'Muscle,' she corrected him quietly. 'You've put on muscle.' And she didn't want to feel pity for him, compassion, but she did. He'd once been so dear, so loved, and was now so impossibly distant.

He removed the jacket, hung it back on the hanger and turned to look at her. 'Help me,' he said quietly. 'Tell me what I was like. I feel as though I don't exist. That I never existed. My only memories are of a dirty cargo ship, of rough men in rough places. I look at you and I don't *know* you. We presumably kissed, made love…'

Turning away, she forced herself to sound flat, uninterested. 'Yes.' But her heart wasn't uninterested, or her mind.

'But I don't *remember* it!' Rubbing a hand across his forehead, he gave a tired sigh.

'Don't try to force it.'

'Why?' he demanded raggedly. 'An expert on head injuries, are you? Know about amnesia? Sorry,' he apologised wearily.

'It's all right. But did you really expect it all to come rushing back when you walked through the door?'

'Yes,' he said slowly. 'I rather thought I did.'

'Then I'm sorry. I'll tell you all I can, *do* all I can, but—'

'But it won't mean anything, will it? The last doctor I saw said something about a mental block I'd put up. For why? Why would I put up a block? What *happened*, Gellis?'

'I don't know.'

'But you're weary of me, aren't you?'

'Trying to hate you,' she said, almost too softly for him to hear. Walking to the window, she stared out over the sea. It was easier if she didn't look at him. 'For fourteen months we were—everything to each other. Or so I thought. I loved you. Heart and soul. I thought you felt the same way about me.'

'And I didn't?'

'Obviously not,' she said slowly.

'But there was no hint of it? I just left one day? Sent you a note? Which said what?'

'That you wouldn't be back.'

'Nothing else? Nothing happened? Was said? Done?' Moving across to her, he slowly turned her, stared down into her lovely face. 'There must be something else! *Must* be! You said you looked for me…'

'Yes. I couldn't believe it, you see. And I needed to know what was going on. And then…'

'Then?' he prompted.

She shook her head. What was the point in telling him about Nathalie? It would only confuse the issue. 'And then I went back to England,' she improvised. Days, weeks of worry, not knowing where he was, what had happened to him. And, in the end, she had tried to resign herself to not ever knowing what had happened, why he had done what he had. She'd got on with her life, because there wasn't only herself to think of, was there? And she couldn't tell him about his son, could she? Not now.

And so, for the moment, until she came to terms with this new Sébastien, she would keep quiet, tell him only about their life together, how it had been before he'd left. Glancing up at him, she saw that he was frowning—not really seeing her, she thought, only trying to part a veil that would not part.

'You said I was kind, humorous…'

'Yes.'

'Tell me how. Instances, *something*. *Help* me, Gellis! What was I *like*? What did I *do*? How did I *behave*? I look at you, and I can't believe I would have forgotten you.' As though unaware of what he was doing, he reached out, gently touched his fingers to her face, looked deep into her eyes. And she held herself stiff, determinedly refused to feel anything. 'You're exquisitely beautiful, and I have a yearning to—kiss you. May I?' he asked huskily.

Her heart suddenly jerked and, with fear and panic inside, a shortness of breath she could do nothing about, she whispered, distressedly, 'Oh, Sébastien…'

'Was that a yes or a no?' he asked with throaty humour. Eyes hypnotically fixed on hers, he dropped his hand to her plait, slowly let it slide down to the bottom. 'You're shaking.'

'Don't do this,' she whispered.

'Beautiful hair,' he continued as though he hadn't heard. 'I have a desire to wind it round your long neck, hold you close…'

'No!' She wrenched free, and he hauled her back, kissed her. Not brutally, not harshly, but like a man who was so very hungry. With a little sound in the back of his throat, he continued to explore her mouth, gently taste the sweetness. And she could do nothing, only stand there, heart beating furiously, throat dry as the warmth of his kiss set up that familiar shudder inside, that spiralling ache that turned her bones to water, her knees to jelly.

She closed her eyes, fought not to react, and felt her mind slowing, her body begin to melt... 'No!' Thrusting him away, she quickly turned her back. 'You mustn't,' she declared shakily. But it was too late, wasn't it? He already had.

'I'm sorry, but— Was that how it was, Gellis? Between us? That—magnetism?'

Wrapping her arms round herself for warmth, comfort, she nodded. 'Yes,' she admitted painfully.

'Then talk to me. Put it into words. Let me see how it was. Please.'

Distraught, embarrassed, frightened of feelings she'd thought she had shut away, she murmured huskily, 'We didn't like to be apart for long. If you missed me...'

'And wouldn't you have missed me?'

'Yes,' she whispered thickly. 'I always missed you. Still miss you.'

'And if I hadn't lost my memory? Hadn't left you? What would we be doing now? Making love?'

'Yes,' she admitted rustily, her whole body aching with the sudden need of it. The memory. 'You would have swept me up when we came through the front door, carried me in here...'

'And made love to you?'

'Yes.'

'Was I a good lover, Gellis?'

'Yes.' Eyes blurring with tears, she choked huskily, 'Oh, Sébastien, you were gentle, funny...'

'*Funny?* Dear God, I don't think I would know how to be funny even if you gave me a manual. Go on, tell me how it was. Make me see it. Set the scene. Pretend it's a play. You've been out shopping, you come back, I'm here—then what? What would I say? Do? *Help* me, Gellis!'

Closing her eyes for a moment, she took a deep breath. 'You would smile— Oh, Sébastien, you had such a wicked smile.'

'Did I?' he asked bleakly.

'Yes.'

'Then what?'

'Oh, you would take my shopping, dump it somewhere, and then you would…' Taking a deep, painful breath, she continued huskily, 'You would take me in your arms. Your eyes would be alight with laughter, and then you would kiss me as though you hadn't seen me in weeks, and—'

'How?' he interrupted. 'Gently? Passionately? How?'

'Does it *matter*?'

'Yes! How?'

Face still averted, she whispered sadly, 'You would start at the corner of my mouth, all the time whispering…' Whispering and urging, his voice at variance with the devilish laughter in his eyes. And always in French; he'd only ever made love to her in French. Fresh tears in her eyes, she whispered in anguish, 'Oh, Sébastien, I can't!'

Touching her shoulder, he gently turned her. 'Yes, you can. Please. I know I'm hurting you… Dear God, Gellis, what sort of a bastard *was* I to make you hurt so much?'

'I don't *know*!' she cried. 'That's what I find so hard! That's what hurts so! I didn't *know*! I thought you were so special, so different, and all the time…'

Closing her eyes tight, she took a deep breath. 'I'm sorry. But I find this so hard.'

'Yes,' he agreed emptily. 'You think I was living a lie? Pretending to love you?'

'Yes,' she agreed painfully.

'But why?'

'I don't know. I don't know why anyone would do that. Or perhaps you did love me,' she added softly. 'Certainly that would be less hurtful to believe—and then maybe you got cold feet, felt trapped. I don't know, Sébastien, but whatever the reasons it was a coward's way out to write me a note.'

'Yes,' he agreed grimly.

'And yet I wouldn't ever have said you were a coward.'

'And so it goes round and round in your mind, with no answers. Just like mine.'

'Yes,' she said with a small attempt at a smile.

'And I don't think smiling at me is a very good idea,' he reproved her with ironic humour. 'I've been celibate for four months at least. And I don't think celibacy is my natural inclination.'

'No,' she said awkwardly, her face pink.

'Go on. What did I whisper?'

'Suggestions.'

'*Suggestions?* What sort of suggestions?'

With an embarrassed shrug, she murmured, 'Erotic.'

'*Erotic?*'

'Yes.'

A sudden glimmer of amusement in his eyes, he asked, 'And then what?'

'Stop it!' she cried. 'Oh, stop it! Don't you see that I'm trying to *hate* you?'

'Yes,' he agreed bleakly. 'I do see that. I see a woman torn, much as my mind is torn, and I don't think I can bear the thought that I will never remember. That for the rest of my life I will be lost in this land of shadows.'

'No,' she agreed helplessly.

And then he smiled, a small smile, almost a Sébastien smile. 'Perhaps you shouldn't have told me about the erotic suggestions. I now have a desperate yearning to whisper some to you.'

Expression sobering, he searched her eyes, her face. 'I have no memory of you, and yet—something tugs at me. A feeling of warmth, peace, need—and arousal,' he added softly. 'On the long drive here, staring out at scenery that meant nothing, I was only aware of you beside me—the faint scent of your perfume, your warmth—and I wanted you to stop the car, face me, touch me. Inappropriate, hmm?'

She didn't answer, couldn't answer, because the same arousal was burning in her. She wanted him. Wanted the nightmare to go away.

'You feel it too, don't you?'

'Yes,' she admitted honestly. 'But it can't be, can it?'

'Can't it?'

'No.'

'For why?'

'Because...' Searching his face, his dear face—a face that no longer looked harsh, just sad—she continued, 'Because I couldn't go through it all again. Supposing, just supposing, we did get back together. Supposing it was as good as it had been—and then supposing you got your memory back. What then, Sébastien?'

With a bleak smile, he said quietly, 'I would then know why I had left you. And maybe leave again.'

'Yes. And I couldn't go through that. Not twice.'

'No.' Watching her, feeling so many conflicting emotions, he said quietly, 'You still love me, don't you?'

With a smile that was wry and sad, heartbreaking to behold, she nodded. 'Tell me how to stop, Sébastien. Tell me how.' Long lashes hiding her eyes, she turned away. 'I'll go and pour the coffee.' But if it hadn't been for Nathalie... No, she denied even more firmly; she really couldn't go through it all again. And no matter how much it hurt, how much her heart felt broken, she had the baby to think of, and so she must be strong.

When he eventually came out, she was sitting on the rear balcony huddled in her leather jacket, nursing a cold cup of coffee. She'd rung her mother, let her know she'd arrived safely, promised to let her know when she was returning home.

'I went through all the drawers,' he said quietly as he came out with his own coffee. 'And then through the papers in the bureau in the lounge. The bank statements only go up to January...'

'Do they?'

'Yes, but it seems I've a very wealthy man.'

'Yes,' she agreed without telling him *why* the bank statements only went up to January.

'I'll ring the bank tomorrow, go and see the manager.'

'Yes. You should also go and see your lawyer. He's been keeping an eye on things for you.'

'And on you?' he asked quietly.

'We keep in touch. Are you hungry?'

'Not especially. We can eat out late. Save cooking.'

'Yes.' And once, not so very long ago, he would have done the cooking. He liked to cook. Had, she mentally corrected.

'I think I'll go for a walk,' he announced abruptly. 'Stretch my legs.'

'All right.'

He gave a small grimace, placed his cup carefully on the wrought-iron table and went quietly out.

When he returned, she was still sitting on the rear porch, staring towards the sea. She smiled at him, a mechanical movement of her mouth, and he smiled back—but it wasn't Sébastien's smile, it was the smile of a stranger.

'Did I know everyone in the town?' he asked quietly as he came to sit opposite her. 'Everywhere I went, everywhere I walked, people called to me, clapped me on the back, asked about—this.' Fingering the white stripe of hair, he glanced at her. 'Is this where we met? Here in Collioure?'

'Yes, at the café on the front next to the sandy area where they play *boules*. It was the first day of my holiday.'

'And I was living here?'

'Yes.'

He sighed, and, when he asked nothing more, she said quietly, 'I'll get us something to eat.'

'You don't want to go out?'

She shook her head. With a long sigh of her own, she returned inside. And, as though programmed, as though no time had passed, she walked into the lounge, depressed the button on the tape deck, and gave a faint, sad smile when his favourite music spilled forth. Debussy.

Gellis then prepared a light meal, but neither of them ate very much. And all that long evening she watched his pain and confusion, his frustration, avoided his eyes when he looked at her—and he looked at her often. And, as the hours ticked by, the tension became greater, until she could stand it no longer. Almost jumping to her feet, she declared abruptly, 'I think I'll go to bed. Goodnight, Sébastien.'

'Goodnight,' he said bleakly.

The next day was worse. Tension became almost a physical entity, and, after a first accidental touching when they had both reached for something at the same time, they carefully did not touch again. They also avoided eye contact, because both knew what would happen if contact were ever made.

The constant stream of visitors didn't help—shopkeepers, barmen, yachtsmen from Port Vendres. Word had spread about his accident and they all came to see him, exclaim, commiserate. And it all put more and more pressure on him because he remembered none of them. His smile, on the rare occasions when he *did* smile, was strained. As was Gellis's.

'I ought to go home,' she finally suggested quietly.

He looked at her, looked away. 'You said a few days.'

'I know, but...'

'Please.'

'And now that you know everyone again...'

'No. Please. You're the only one who can tell me what I need to know.'

And the terrible thing was, she didn't *want* to go. But it would be a fool's paradise. And she couldn't stay in this small apartment with him any longer, not being able to touch, talk. And to lie each night just a few yards away from him was purgatory. She had thought she could be strong—and she couldn't. Not any more. She wanted him, wanted his warmth, his lovemaking, his laughter, was beginning not to care what he had done. Just to have him back again.

No. She must go home. 'One more day,' she finally agreed. 'I still have my Christmas shopping to do…'

'You could do it here.'

'No. I have to go home. But for now we need bread, eggs…'

'I'll go.'

She shook her head. 'I need some fresh air.' Hastily escaping, she walked into the town. These were my friends, she thought sadly as she vaguely smiled at people, waved to shopkeepers. And now everyone looks awkward, embarrassed, doesn't know what to say. She could see pity for her in their eyes, compassion, but there was nothing anyone could do, including herself.

And, when she came back, he was sitting at the kitchen table. The photograph album was beside him, a stack of snapshots spread out before him. But not those of their wedding. She had those with her in England. Along with the pictures of their son.

He looked up, gave a half-smile, explained, 'I found them in the dining room. When were these taken? Last summer?'

'Yes.'

'I look so damned young.'

'Thirty-five.'

'Yes,' he agreed with a twisted smile. 'What a difference a year makes. I don't even know how old *you* are.'

'Twenty-eight.'

Holding one snap between his fingers, he stared at it for some moments in silence. 'You look—different. Happy.' Flipping it round, he showed it to her.

Slowly taking it, she stared at herself, at the laughing girl in the flowing summer dress, at the long, dark hair cascading loose—as Sébastien had liked it. No inkling then of what was to come. No shadows to mar their happiness.

'Where was it taken?'

'Ermitage something or other. Up in the Pyrenees.'

'Looks a gloomy sort of place.'

'Yes, it was. An old monastery—something religious anyway. The chapel was all neglected, the floor tiles broken and uneven. Dark. Unloved. No birds sang there, and the trees had grown over the courtyard...'

And she'd been laughing because they'd been interrupted. Unable to leave each other alone, unable to stop touching, she had leaned him against a tree, slowly undone his shirt buttons, had begun placing soft, erotic little kisses on his chest—and arousal had been a heartbeat away when another couple had arrived. She'd spun away, laughing, and he'd snatched up the camera and taken that picture of her.

With a faint, sad smile, she handed it back, reached for another. One of him. She stared at it for a long time, remembering. 'You were—delightful,' she murmured softly. 'Charming, slightly wicked, very—French.'

'I sound like an imbecile.'

'No,' she denied gently. Slowly replacing the photograph, she looked at him. Not an imbecile. Just a cheat and a coward. But she hadn't known that then.

With a long sigh, he shuffled the photographs into a tidy pile—and then spread them out again. 'Tell me about it. How we met.'

'All right,' she agreed quietly. 'Would you like some coffee first?'

He nodded, and she got up to switch on the percolator, get out the cups. Last day, she told herself. Tomorrow she would go home. *Had* to go home. Nerves were getting rubbed too raw; tension was sometimes only a moment away from explosion.

Standing behind him, waiting for the coffee to heat, she watched him. Watched a back she had touched. Hair she had ruffled. She tried to contain the pain. It would be so easy to give in. So easy to love, and, if only the rest of the world didn't exist, if there were only this small pinpoint of light in a universe unseen, unknown...

And, suddenly, there was such a flood of longing for this man, this one man who had turned her world upside down. She wanted so desperately to slide her arms round him, press a kiss to his temple, and he would turn, pull her onto his lap... But it was a longing that must be denied. She couldn't afford to risk her sanity again.

Muscles tight, blinking back tears, she poured the coffee and carried it to the table. Seating herself opposite him, palms curved round her cup, eyes lowered, she thought about what to say.

CHAPTER FOUR

'WE MET in Franco's,' Gellis murmured. A café divided by a road. Tables and chairs one side, establishment on the other, and she'd smiled in amusement as she'd watched the waiter dodge the traffic, tray held high above his head. Unaware that she, in turn, was being watched by most of the people seated around her, she'd tilted her face to the sun and given a long sigh of satisfaction. One whole month in which to enjoy all the delights of the south of France. A month of lazy days, going where she wanted when she wanted.

She'd worn a white silk skirt, she remembered, and white trousers, her long, dark hair piled loosely on top of her head, dark glasses perched on her nose.

I looked up,' she said quietly, 'and there you were. A so very attractive Frenchman. Attention focused on your paper, I studied you at leisure. Ruffled dark hair that just brushed the neck of your white T-shirt, broad shoulders, a very attractive nose, and a mouth made for—passion.'

With a quirky little smile, part embarrassment, part memory, she continued, 'I couldn't see your eyes, only the dark lashes—until you looked up unexpectedly and caught me staring. You didn't look away, and I felt unable to. We exchanged a long, long look that went on for eternity. A look that said, I find you attractive. A look that reciprocated. The waiter walked between us, and the spell was broken. Almost broken.'

'It sounds like the worst romantic novel ever written.'

'Yes,' she agreed sadly. 'But that was how it was. You came over to my table, asked if I knew you.'

'*Déjà vu.*'

'Yes.'

Eyes distant, he tried to stare into a past that was no longer there, then slowly drew the photograph album in front of him towards him, began to turn the pages.

Watching him, aching for him, she moved her eyes to his mouth, remembered their first kiss. First *proper* kiss. The promise of it had been with her for weeks, but the actuality of it, the power, had robbed her of breath. Day after day they had met and toured the Pyrenees together in her car because he no longer had one. He had sold it along with everything else when he'd moved to Collioure.

Hill-top villages, castles, forts, shopping in Perpignan. And, at the end of each day, he would stop the car at the top of the hill that led into Collioure, and they would both get out—he to leave, she to take the driving seat. He would hold her shoulders, smile his wicked smile and kiss her gently on each cheek. Then he'd walk home whilst she drove the short distance to her rented apartment feeling unutterably frustrated. And then, two weeks after they had first met, he had finally kissed her on the mouth.

After endless days of warm sun, blue skies, the weather had changed, become unsettled. A wind had sprung up, bringing dark clouds, and everyone had been pleased. They'd had no rain for months, and everywhere was parched and dry. Gellis and Sébastien had eaten early and were sitting beneath the awning outside a café in Port Vendres having a last drink before going back to their separate apartments.

It had been a gentle sound at first, just a sighing breeze that had tinkled the rigging of the yachts, soughed through the branches of the trees that lined the yacht basin. And then the rain had begun, gentle at first, bringing everyone out to test it on their hands and upturned faces, and then a downpour that had chased everyone back inside.

She'd smiled at him, and he'd smiled lazily back. Heart turning in her breast, she'd known she didn't ever want to go home. Leave him. But he hadn't felt the same... Hadn't *thought* he felt the same.

'We're going to get wet,' she murmured inanely.

'Mmm.'

'The car's at the other end of the port.'

'Mmm.'

Feeling a splash on her cheek, she looked up and gave a rueful smile as she saw the canopy above them filling with water. Then jumped when a fierce gust of wind blew a couple of chairs over, sent the yachts' rigging into a shrieking frenzy. People were beginning to scurry past, newspapers over their heads, rushing for the nearest shelter, and Gellis and Sébastien sat and watched it all.

'Tail-end of the hurricane they've been having in the States.'

'Is it?'

'Mmm,' he confirmed in amusement.

Shivering a little in the cooler air, she huddled into her light jacket, and he reached out, pulled her against his side. Shared the warmth of his body with her. She looked up into his face, and desire flooded through her at the warmth she saw in his eyes. Warmth and something else.

'Time to go,' he said softly, and she swallowed the dryness in her throat, managed a nod. Was this it? Finally, at last? Because she would soon be going home and there could be no—recriminations? She didn't know. Didn't think she cared.

Finishing his drink, he placed his empty glass on the table and waited.

Quickly finishing her own, heartbeat faster, a racing excitement inside, she stood with him, his arm still round her, and he smiled.

'Ready?'

'Yes,' she agreed huskily.

Withdrawing his arm from her shoulder, his hand never left contact as he slid his open palm down her arm and clasped her hand in warm fingers. Everything he did seemed slow, deliberate, well thought out. Would his lovemaking be the same? Feeling heat rush through her, she took a moment to realise he'd asked a question. Glancing up at him, hair and clothing whipped by a mischievous wind, she whispered, 'What?'

He smiled, slowly, his eyes amused. 'I asked if you can run.'

'Oh, yes.'

'*Bien*. Let's go.'

Hands clasped firmly, they sprinted through the arch formed by restaurant awnings, dodged other people similarly engaged, and, laughing breathlessly, emerged at the bottom of the hill.

Soaked, wind-whipped, laughing as though it were the biggest joke ever invented, he pulled her across the road and into the car park. And as they reached her car he swung her round—and into his arms.

As he stared down into her laughing face, hair plastered to his skull, rain dripping from his elegant nose, his smile slowly died. Smoothing his palms up her wet body, he framed her face and slowly lowered his head to kiss her. To slowly kiss her. Taste the raindrops on her lips, gently dry them with his own.

It was maybe only meant to be a swift kiss, born of laughter and exertion, but it didn't end up that way. Warmed by the heat of him, the feel of him, she wound her arms round his waist, held him tight, parted her mouth and kissed him back with a need that had been building to unbearable proportions over the past few weeks of his company.

Breathing ragged, unsteady from the gusting wind that threatened to tear her loose from him, she clung tight, stood with feet apart for balance and revelled in a pleasure as old as time.

Eventually, what seemed a very long time later, he slowly raised his head and stared at her. The street lamp behind her showed lashes beaded with moisture that sparkled like tears, highlighted the planes and angles of a face marked by strength and humour. The high walls beside them cut off some of the wind, but not enough to still the collar of his shirt that was plastered wetly to his chest, not enough to leave his dark hair unruffled.

'Kissing in the rain should be included in the manual,' he whispered softly, and his accent was deeper, sexier, throaty. 'Kissing in the rain should be—compulsory. Take me home, my friend.'

'You want me to drive?'

'*Oui.*'

'All the way?'

'*Oui.*'

Swallowing hard, she fumbled her bag from her shoulder, groped for her keys, and, with reluctance, left the warmth of his body for the cold interior of the car.

Shivering, she turned on the engine, pushed the heater lever to high, switched on the blower and gave a foolish smile as he climbed in beside her. Never before had he asked her to take him home. Never before had he allowed her to drive—except when he stopped each night at the top of the hill. But not tonight. Tonight it was raining. And so she would take him home.

It seemed to take forever for the windscreen to demist, an eternity of sitting beside him not knowing what to say. And, when he touched gentle fingers to her cold cheek, she jumped, gave a nervous laugh. 'It's harder,' she said foolishly.

'What is harder, Gellis?' he asked gently.

'The rain.'

'Yes.'

'And the wind. Definitely seems stronger, don't you think?'

'Yes.'

Oh, God. And she wanted to turn to him, burrow against his warmth. Slowly remove his clothes. With a little shudder, she said almost inaudibly, 'I don't know where you live.'

'I'll direct you.'

Yes. Hands shaking, unable to wait any longer, she shoved the gear lever into reverse and quickly backed out. If there had been anything behind her, she would have hit it because she could see absolutely nothing through the rear windscreen.

'Lights?' he prompted. He sounded as though he was smiling.

Feeling a fool, unbearably aware of the hard thigh beside her own, the arm next to hers, she quickly switched on the headlights and drove up the slight incline to the road. Nothing was coming, and she drove out and up the hill like a novice.

Bent forward, peering through the rain-lashed windscreen, she drove cautiously, the wipers on fast setting. Past the garage, the apartments, a few lights flickering here and there, and then down into the town.

'Keep going, up to the junction, then right and first left. There's a small car park that serves my apartment.'

With a jerky nod, heart beating uncomfortably fast, she did as she was told. It was now a wild night; the trees along the front were thrashing to and fro as though trying to escape, the sea a dull roar as it pounded the tiny beach.

Driving across the bridge, she could see on the periphery of her vision the water racing down the culvert below them, hoped no one had left their car parked there. The few cafés and bars still open were hastily putting up their storm shutters, chaining their tables and chairs together for safety, taking down wildly flapping awnings.

'Right, did you say?'

'*Oui.*' And when she reached the car park would he merely get out, say goodnight?

'Left here,' he prompted.

'Yes, sorry.'

Pulling into the tiny car park, a car park that was rapidly flooding, she glanced at him in query.

'Drive to the back; the ground is slightly higher, and there's a run-off. The car will be fine.'

She drove cautiously through the deep puddles and parked where he indicated. She switched off the engine and lights.

He picked up her bag from between his feet and silently handed it to her.

She stared at him, her eyes wide and slightly worried, and he stared back. Waited. And then he smiled, invited teasingly, 'Coffee?'

With a nervous laugh, and a nod, and a quick glance at the sheeting rain, she murmured, 'On the count of three?'

He nodded, and agreed solemnly, 'On the count of three. *Un, deux, trois…*' Unlatching their doors, they scrambled out, slammed them, and Gellis quickly shoved the key into the lock and twisted it.

Beaten down by rain that hurt, eyes squeezed nearly shut, they grabbed hands and ran. Jumping over a large puddle, they splashed up a narrow cobbled alley, skidded across a small square and, laughing, unbelievably wet, Sébastien dragged her up a few steps and thrust her through a doorway.

The darkness was complete as he closed the door behind them. Velvety, with a faint aroma of—lemons? She could feel him behind her, and, if she held her breath, hear his soft breathing—not erratic like her own. There was a familiar sensation in her tummy, a squirmy, half-frightening, half-pleasurable feeling. Her back to him, hands gripping her bag, she waited for whatever was to come.

'Welcome to my home,' he said softly, and his breath stirred the hair on the back of her neck.

'Thank you,' she said huskily.

Hands touched her shoulders, felt the wetness of her jacket, and he added quietly, 'Go get out of those wet things. Bathroom's to your right. I'll go and make the coffee.'

There was a click, and soft light illuminated the rust-coloured tiles on the floor, the stark white walls. A framed pencil sketch of a fort hung to her left.

'Use the robe on the bathroom door. There's a pull-switch just inside.'

With a nod, she scurried into the room he had indicated, jerked on the light and closed the door behind her. A large mirror above the washbasin faced her, and she stared at herself for some moments in shock. She looked—aroused. Wet—and wanton. Anticipatory. Looking hastily away from a face that seemed unfamiliar, she stared round her.

Grey and white tiles covered the floor, grey surrounds to the bath and basin. Dark green towels hung on a rail beside the shower cubicle—and she was dripping. Had, in fact, made a small puddle. Easing off her low-heeled sandals, she stripped off her jacket, and, not knowing where else to put it, dropped it on the floor. With a little shiver, she stripped off her blouse and skirt and dropped them to join her jacket.

Her underwear was also sopping wet, and uncomfortable. Biting her lip for a moment in indecision, she finally shrugged and removed them. Opening the shower cabinet, she pulled the lever and held out her hand to test the water. When it ran hot, she stepped in and closed the door.

Five minutes later, feeling warmed and less shaky,

she switched it off, climbed out and rubbed herself dry before donning Sébastien's navy towelling robe that hung behind the door. After rolling up the over-long sleeves and securely tying the belt, she picked up her wet clothes and hesitantly emerged. Taking a deep breath, she padded to the far end of the hall.

Peeping into the kitchen, she saw Sébastien, watched him get out heavy mugs. He'd changed into grey trousers and a grey sweatshirt, his hair towelled roughly dry. His feet were bare. As though aware of being watched, he suddenly turned, smiled.

'Here, give me your wet things; I'll dry them in the oven.'

'In the *oven*?' she queried in astonishment, and he grinned.

'In *front* of the oven,' he corrected with another small smile. 'And you look very fetching in my robe,' he added softly.

Before she could think of a reply, he walked across to collect a small airer from the corner. Setting it up in front of the oven, he switched the oven on and opened the door. Walking over to her, he dropped a swift kiss on her mouth, removed her wet clothes from her and draped them carefully over the airer. There was something rather disturbing about watching a man carefully arrange her underwear. Averting her eyes, she stared round the small kitchen. White, ochre, brown, the same floor tiles as the hall. She felt very young.

'Go into the lounge,' he ordered softly. 'I'll bring the coffee through.'

Hastily retreating, she walked through the open door into the lounge. There was a square of carpet laid on polished boards, a sofa, two armchairs, table and four chairs. Nothing spectacular, nothing special—functional and comfortable. Net curtains framed the large window, and she walked across to stare at his view. And smiled.

The illuminated fort on top of the hill looked as though it was floating like a fairy castle in mid-air. Nothing could be seen of the hill, just a wavering reflection of the fort. Rain beat against the windows, wind howled round the building and, if she listened very carefully, she could hear the crash of waves on the rocks.

'Here,' he said from behind her, and she jumped, turned to give him a lame smile.

He set the mugs down on the coffee-table and waited for her to walk across, seat herself on the sofa. Amusement playing about his mouth, he drew the nets across the windows but left the heavy curtains undrawn. And then he walked back—and sat beside her on the couch. Close beside her.

'Hello,' he greeted softly, and she flicked him a startled glance.

Wicked laughter danced in his eyes, a fascinating smile played round his mouth. But there was tension too—she could *feel* it—and when he reached out, touched a gentle finger to her cheek, she sucked in her breath hard. Eyes enormous, she just stared at him.

He smiled, leaned back and draped one arm along the couch at her back. Jerking her head to the front, she stared at her coffee-mug as though mesmerised. So very aware of him, senses so very heightened, she remained rigid until he lifted his hand and touched the base of her plait.

'I have had a fantasy,' he said in a soft, magnetic

voice, the accent pronounced. 'That I grasp this so very convenient plait, just—here,' he murmured seductively as he grasped the plait more firmly so that his fingers touched against her neck, making her shiver. Warm fingers—*hot* fingers. 'And pull you into my arms. My prisoner, my captive. And then I slowly, oh, so slowly unravel it—like this…' Both hands on her hair, he began to tease the strands free whilst she sat like a very agitated statue.

'And when I have undone all of it, when it hangs to your hips in a shining, though damp curtain,' he murmured, that smile back in his voice, 'why, then— then I have you entirely in my power. And the only way to escape is to cut off all this glorious hair.' His long fingers combing and combing until every strand hung straight, he slowly grasped a handful, again at her neck, and gently pulled.

Unresisting, breathless, Gellis toppled back against him, and he moved, settled her in the corner of the sofa, took two handfuls of her long, long hair. That he bunched it up, admired the effect, let it slide through his strong fingers, eyes fixed on what he was doing, then began all over again—and then he looked at her, deep into her eyes, held her hair either side of her exquisite face, spread his fingers against her scalp and promised softly, 'Now I am going to kiss you. Kiss you the way I have wanted to kiss you since— oh, since I saw you in that café when you looked up and didn't look away. As you can't look away now. Can you?'

She swallowed, gave the faintest shake of her head—all she could manage. Mesmerised, hypnotised, his voice a seductive murmur, she could do nothing but—comply. Do nothing but watch his mouth come closer, and, when he went out of focus, close her eyes and wait. But not for long. Only eternity. When his mouth finally touched hers, she took a snatched little breath, made the tiniest sound in her throat, and gave in to—magic. His mouth was warm and dry, experienced, and, when he had kissed her entirely to his own satisfaction and hers, he raised his head, smiled into her sleepy eyes.

'Good?'

'Yes,' she whispered.

'*Bon*. Then now you may kiss me. If that is your wish.'

It was. She couldn't think of any other wish she wanted fulfilled more. A hand on each of his wrists, she slid her hands slowly up to his elbows, his shoulders, touched her fingers to his neck, slid them into his hair and urged him back towards her, parted his mouth and kissed him as he had kissed her. Not so experienced, not so expert, but satisfactory nevertheless.

And when the kisses had gone on longer than kisses should be allowed to do, when urgency began to replace languor, he lifted his head, smiled only with his eyes and lifted his legs onto the sofa. Urging her down, he tucked her in beside him, rearranged the robe over her long legs when it parted and put his head on the cushion so that he lay slightly above her. Reaching for her hair, he smoothed it over her left shoulder, then began winding it round and round into a spiral. When he was satisfied with the effect, he poked the end into the neck of the robe between her breasts.

'I won't touch,' he murmured throatily, and with an abominably wicked smile. 'But I can touch the hair that touched. Can't I?' Withdrawing it, he held it to his mouth, eyes never once leaving hers—and then replaced it.

Why wouldn't he touch? she wondered. She wanted him to. Had never wanted anything so much in all her life.

'Does it tickle?' he asked wickedly.

Unable to speak, unable to do anything but stare at him, feel her own nakedness beneath the robe—a nakedness she wanted to share—she managed a jerky nod. And he pushed it further until the soft ends of her hair touched her stomach, and she felt—boneless. Completely and utterly helpless.

'Tell me about you,' he persuaded softly, seductively, huskily. 'About your life and loves— No,' he amended with a quirky smile. 'Not about your loves. Tell me about your hopes, dreams. Tell me what you want.'

Tell him? She didn't think she could tell him anything. She didn't think she could speak. And there had been only one past love, and he had died.

CHAPTER FIVE

'GELLIS?'

With a blink, she focused on Sébastien—a different Sébastien. One with a sterner face, a badge of white at one temple. And he frowned.

'What is it? What were you thinking? You look so…'

With a little shudder, her eyes filmed with tears, she shook her head. 'Nothing,' she whispered. 'I was just—thinking. Remembering. What do you feel,' she asked slowly, 'when you look at me?'

'Desire,' he said thickly. 'I find it very hard to be with you and not touch. You see? I am being honest. And my mind—imagines. Sends disastrously tempting pictures of you naked, of us entwined on the bed…'

'Oh, please don't,' she pleaded in distress.

'Non,' he agreed sombrely. 'But I want so much to feel as I once presumably felt, and I want to know why I hurt you. I think I want to know that more than anything.' Lowering his eyes, he stared blindly at the photographs spread out before him.

'After the accident,' he resumed slowly, 'I was almost afraid to make enquiries. Supposing I was a murderer? A rapist? Fraud, embezzlement…' With a grim smile, he looked up at her. 'I went to the records office in Paris and, starting with the date of my accident, read through all the newspapers I could find.

And when nothing came to light, no "wanted" posters, not even, it seemed, any speculation, I was…'

'Miffed?' she asked gently.

'Miffed? Yes, miffed,' he agreed with a glimmer of amusement. 'A man of no importance. Not even missed. There's arrogance for you. And then I thought perhaps I *wasn't* French, but French Canadian, French something else… Let's go out,' he added almost urgently.

'Out?'

'Yes. I think it is best to—keep busy. We can walk where we walked, sit where we sat, talk how we talked. I can't go on like this, day after day, not knowing, perhaps never knowing. I have to do *something* to jog my memory, take away this pain. And if we sit here much longer just looking at each other I fear seduction *will* be on my mind.'

But it wouldn't *be* seduction, would it? If he touched her, she would give in. Almost frightened by her feelings, she got quickly to her feet, led the way out.

'Did we hold hands?' he asked with rather bleak mockery as they walked into the town.

'Yes.'

When he caught her hand in his, she stiffened, then carefully released it.

'Not a good idea?'

'No,' she replied shakily. Tomorrow morning she would go home. She must. She couldn't take much more of this.

He smiled at people who smiled at him, just a vague movement of his mouth, really, but a sort of smile; he lifted a languid hand when he was waved

t, and the bleakness in his eyes didn't alter one little
it.

Without any clear destination in mind, they walked
past the hotel, down past the cafés, stood by the fort
and idly watched a group of teenagers kicking a ball
about on the damp sand. And the sky now was as
blue as it had been then, but the air was cooler, the
sun not as bright.

They watched artists at work, admired their paint-
ings, drank endless cups of coffee in endless cafés.
But, without memory, it was all meaningless.

'Did I paint?'

Surprised, she shook her head.

'It's an artists' colony.'

'Yes.'

'So why did I come here?'

'I don't know,' she responded helplessly.

'You didn't know much about me at all, did you?'

Hesitating for a brief moment, she shook her head
again. 'No, I didn't know very much about you.' Why
hadn't she asked? she wondered. Why had she never
been curious about why he had sold everything up,
cut all ties with his past?

'I never took you back to where I came from?'

'No. On our trips out we always went into the
mountains or Spain, never towards Nice.'

'And you weren't ever curious? Never asked why?'

Curious? Had she been? She didn't know. She had
accepted him as he was. Had loved him as he was.
And that was odd, she supposed, now that she came
to think about it. 'We were so wrapped up in each
other, so...'

'In love?'

'Yes.'

He turned to give her a discouraged smile. 'So what else did we do?'

'Toured the château.'

'Then let us tour the château,' he urged with grim humour. 'You never know…'

Hurting and unhappy, there was very little trace of the girl he had fallen in love with. No trace of the humour that had captivated him, the teasing smile, the laughter. She felt as she had felt six years ago, when David had died. A two-time loser, because this felt as though Sébastien had died. Or she had.

Walking up the cobbled ramp into the Château Royal, she tried to remember every detail of that other day. Tried to re-create how she had felt. But, of course, she couldn't, because the difference between them and now seemed like an unbridgeable chasm. 'We had a leaflet,' she said quietly.

'Then let us, by all means, collect a leaflet.'

'Don't mock.'

'Sorry.'

Collecting one, with a rather sad smile for the woman behind the desk, she led him on a tour of the château, read out the descriptions as she had then. His French hadn't been very good when they had originally come, and he had laughed at her excruciating accent. He didn't laugh today—and her accent was no longer excruciating. '*La Fausse-Braie fût, élevé à partir de 1669, constituant ainsi un étage de défense sur des salles médiévaux, aujourd'hui souterrain.*'

He grunted.

She didn't bother to read out any more. When they reached the ramparts, hope had given way to desperation. And, when she saw the rose bushes planted all along one wall, remembered the scent when they had been in flower, tears filled her eyes. He had broken off a fading bloom, carefully removed the thorns and tucked it behind one of her ears. And kissed her. He was always kissing her. Any excuse, any reason—as she had kissed him.

Forcibly banishing the memories, she walked on, then halted. 'We stood here,' she announced quietly. 'We were the only ones up here.' A gentle breeze had fanned her hair, caressed her cheeks—as he had caressed her. Stood behind her, encircled her with his arms, and caressed her.

'What is it that you aren't telling me, Gellis?' Sébastien asked quietly.

That you asked me to marry you. Here, on this very spot, you asked me to be your wife. Slowly turning, she stared into his bleak face. 'Nothing,' she lied. 'What makes you think there is?'

His face set, serious, he continued, 'You start explanations then abandon them. You...' Frowning thoughtfully, dark hair ruffled by the fitful breeze, he continued, 'There's tension between us, which I have to admit is mostly sexual.' He added with a strained smile, 'And don't deny it. I might have lost my memory but a man knows when his feelings are— reciprocated.'

'Yes,' she agreed helplessly. Because they were.

'I hurt you, badly, which doesn't alter the fact that we're both fighting it. But it's more than that. What else happened, Gellis?'

Turning away from him, she stared out over the sea. 'Nathalie,' she said quietly.

'Nathalie?'

'Yes. Just after I got your note, she turned up on my doorstep. She was looking for you.'

Turning her back to face him, he stared down into her drawn face, asked quietly, 'You knew her?'

'No.'

'Go on.'

With a deep sigh, she stared at his throat, at the weave of his thick sweater. 'She was very charming, very—distraught. She said she was sorry to bother me, but she wasn't sure which was your apartment. She said you had been going to meet with her, but that you hadn't turned up. She said—you'd asked her to marry you,' she concluded painfully.

'Whilst I was still seeing you? Living with you?' he asked blankly.

'Yes. That you had been seeing each other all summer, that you were—lovers.' Glancing up into his eyes, she registered his shock.

'*Mon Dieu,*' he whispered. 'What sort of man *was* I?'

'I don't know. I wish I did.'

'Why didn't you tell me this before?'

'Because I didn't think it would help. Because you had enough to worry about.' Because I was jealous. Because I hated her. 'I can only assume you didn't meet her because you went to South America instead.'

'And lost my memory.'

'Yes.' Eyes bigger, darker, she whispered unsteadily, 'You think I find this any easier than you? You lost your memory, but I lost—' Breaking off, unable to take any more, she mumbled thickly, 'I'm going home.'

Hurrying away, she stumbled on the stairs, cried when he caught her plait where it touched her neck.

'What? *What?*' he demanded as he twisted her to face him, hand still bunched in her hair.

'That was how you… Always you…'

'What?'

'Held me,' she managed thickly. 'Always you held me like that—this. Used my hair as an anchor.' Staring up into his eyes, searching them, trying to find just one small spark of the man he had been, she cried, 'Oh, Sébastien, I can't take any more of this. I *can't*!' Slumping in his hold, she rested her forehead against his shoulder, clenched her hands tight in his sweater. And he slid his arms round her, held her, rested his head against her own.

'You think I can?' Eyes bleak, he asked quietly, 'Did you tell her who you were?'

'No, not then. I was just numb.' Disbelieving. Seeing pictures of them in her mind. Of Nathalie doing to him what *she* had done to him. Of him… With a long shudder, forcing the visions aside, she murmured, 'She came back a week later. She'd obviously been making enquiries, because then she knew.'

'I see. And where is she now? This Nathalie?''

Voice muffled against his chest, she whispered, 'I don't know. I don't know anything about her, only what I saw. Elegant, blonde, French.' And her hands wanted to slide beneath his sweater, feel the warm flesh beneath… And it was so *hard*. He'd treated them both badly, and so there should have been a bond. But there hadn't been. She had *hated* the other woman.

'You haven't been in touch with her? Told her you've found me?'

'No.' He didn't ask why. Perhaps he didn't need to. 'She lives in Provence,' Gellis said listlessly. 'I don't know the address, only her phone number. I don't even know why I kept it. I'll give it to you when we get back.'

'Thank you. I spoke to my lawyer this morning,' he added inconsequentially, 'and I asked him what I had been like.'

Lifting her head, she stared into his face. 'And?'

'And his description of me doesn't tally with yours.'

'I see.'

'You said I was kind.'

'Yes.'

'Gérard said I was ruthless.'

'Did he?'

'Yes. Sounds as though he was right, doesn't it?'

'I don't know. You were never ruthless to *me*.'

'But to others?'

'Not to my knowledge. You could be—arrogant, indifferent…' The warmth of his body against hers made it hard to think, articulate. The warmth of his thigh. If she parted hers just a little bit, she could press it between her own.

'A care for nobody?'

'What? Oh, no—more…' Forcing herself to concentrate, she tried to think of a way to explain. 'You didn't put yourself out for anyone you didn't like.'

'Does anyone?'

'Yes. You could be cutting… Oh, it's so hard to explain! You've always been wealthy, I think, and that brings a certain—confidence. If something interested you, you were enthusiastic. But if it didn't you were indifferent.'

'But not to you.'

'No.'

Searching her face, he looked quickly away, and,

when he spoke, his voice was rougher, thicker. 'Was it my idea to live together?'

With a brief, dispirited laugh, she demanded, 'You think I forced you? Blackmailed you?'

'No,' he denied. 'I was just trying to find out if you were surprised. That I asked you, I mean.'

'No,' she asserted. 'If you'd asked me to go to the moon, I would have. Is it important?'

'I don't know.' Staring beyond her, at the pretty little town, desperately trying to ignore his response to her nearness, he repeated heavily, 'I don't know.'

'And did Gérard tell you anything else?' she asked carefully.

'No, except he hadn't known I was going to South America, or why I might have gone. And don't do that. Dear God, please don't do that.'

Puzzled, aching, she whispered blankly, 'What?'

'You keep rubbing your hand against my chest,' he said thickly.

Horrified, unaware she'd been doing it, she snatched her hand away, bunched it by her side. 'Sorry.' Moving away from him, back turned, she clutched one of the stone crenellations.

Shoving his hands forcefully into his pockets, he gave a grim smile. 'A philanderer, Gellis? A womaniser? A cheat? Don't sound very nice, do I?'

'No, but… It was so *real*!'

With a hollow laugh, he said, 'Good acting?'

'No! No.' Frowning, she stared rigidly ahead.

'Did I tell you I loved you?'

'Yes. *Yes!*' she insisted.

'Often?'

'Yes. We were so *happy*!'

He gave a twisted smile. 'Well, you're certainly better off without me, aren't you?'

'Am I?' she asked dispiritedly. 'I shouldn't have told you about Nathalie, should I? It hasn't helped, just made you more—wretched.'

'I had to know some time; not much point in gilding a snake.'

'No,' she agreed helplessly.

'And I thought I was coping so well, too,' he said with grim humour. 'Not a very nice feeling to find that you don't like yourself. Maybe I should hope that I *don't* get my memory back. Make a change for the better.'

She nodded, didn't know what else to do. 'We'd better go home; they'll be closing soon.'

'Yes.'

Taking her hand from the stonework, she began walking heavily down to the courtyard.

'You didn't like her, did you?' he asked quietly.

'Nathalie? No.'

'Why?'

'I don't know,' she confessed. 'Just something about her that I didn't like. Not fair to judge under the circumstances, I suppose. If she was hurting as much as me...'

'Yes,' he agreed heavily. 'I wonder how many more there are?'

'Oh, don't.'

Halting her, he looked down into her strained face. 'After all I did to you, you still feel—compassion, Gellis?'

'Yes, of course. If you don't remember who you were, what you were like, well, it isn't *you*, is it?'

'Perverted logic, but no, I suppose not.'

Eyes so very sad, so full of pity for him and for herself, she gave a heartbroken smile. 'And now I have to go home.'

'Now?' he asked bleakly.

'Yes.' It had to be now. Now, whilst she still could.

'Then go quickly.'

'Yes. I can't *stay*, Sébastien.'

'I know. I'll miss you. Drive safely. Or I could…'

'No,' she asserted hastily.

'No,' he agreed with a grim smile.

A sudden rush of tears blurring her vision, she turned and walked away. Held the pain in her heart until she could let it go in private.

When she arrived back at the apartment she packed quickly—just stuffed things into her case—and then walked into his room, trailed her hand across his quilt, inhaled the scent of him that still faintly lingered. A quilt beneath which they had loved. And they *had* been in love, she thought tearfully. Not more on one side than the other. He had *adored* her. He'd said so. So how could he have walked away?

Perhaps he just liked women. Couldn't help himself. There were people like that, weren't there? And, for the short time their love lasted, perhaps it *was* real to them. Perhaps they hoped that this time it would last. Yet there had been no hint of that when they had first met in that café, in that long first look they had exchanged…

With a small, rueful smile she'd looked down, moved her spoon in the saucer—and been aware on the periphery of her vision, and with a definitely accelerated heartbeat, that he was folding his paper and getting to his feet. He'd strolled towards her, halted by her table, and she'd looked hesitantly up. He'd smiled.

'You know me?' he asked softly.

Dark eyes wide, she shook her head.

'Ah.'

'Ah?'

He smiled again, a quirky, attractive smile that did delicious things to her pulse rate.

'How did you know I was English?'

'You really wish for me to tell you?'

She shook her head, her own smile a flicker of promise on her delightful mouth. He had nice eyes, she decided—warm and laughing, hazel with little flecks of green.

Tapping his rolled-up newspaper against the table once, he strolled away.

A silly smile on her face, she watched him walk along the front, watched him halt, make a comment to one of the *boules* players, then move on and out of her sight.

'Fool,' she murmured to herself. But she was on holiday, and on holiday foolishness was allowed, wasn't it? Of course it was. And, not at all to her surprise, he lingered in her mind for the rest of that day.

And when she drove into Port Vendres that evening to dine she saw him again. Seated beneath a blue striped awning, enjoying an aperitif before ordering, she watched him jump down from a yacht moored in the basin. He slung a thick sweater over one shoulder, made a laughing rejoinder to the man still on board, halted briefly to allow a car to pass then began to saunter across the road.

He was tall and tanned, lithe and fit, and more than

one woman turned to glance at him. A smile still
played about his mouth, his eyes were creased in
amusement—and then he saw her, and halted. His
smile widened—a wicked, wicked smile—and then he
walked slowly towards her.

'*Bonsoir.*'

'*Bonsoir,*' she echoed, a little quirk to her mouth.

Gazing thoughtfully at her for a moment, a delightful twinkle in his eyes, he gave a slow nod. '*Bien,*'
he murmured softly. 'Shall I join you?' With a minus-
cule shrug, he answered himself. 'Why not? You per-
mit?'

'Certainly,' she agreed.

He smiled, pulled out the chair opposite and sat
down. 'What are you drinking?' Taking the glass from
her hand, he sniffed, pursed his lips in apparent dis-
approval and returned it to her. 'You have deplorable
taste, my friend.' Glancing round for the waiter, he
asked for another glass and a bottle of Chablis. Returning his attention to her, he asked, *Comment vous
appelez-vous?*'

Staring at him, a rueful smile in her eyes, she repeated it over to herself several times, then grinned
triumphantly. 'Gellis Harper.'

'Gellis,' he echoed as though savouring it.

'*Et vous?*' she asked proudly.

'Sébastien Fourcard.'

Oh, nice. Extending her hand, she said softly,
'Hello, Sébastien Fourcard.'

He smiled as though delighted, took her hand and
gently touched her fingers to his lips. Releasing it, he
smiled as the waiter put the ice bucket containing his
wine on the table and placed a glass before him. The
waiter would have poured some into Sébastien's

glass, but Sébastien waved him away. Taking Gellis's glass from her once more, eyes holding hers, he ruthlessly tipped the contents into the ice bucket and poured her a glass of Chablis. 'Try that,' he ordered.

Amused, she sipped the chilled wine, nodded her approval. 'Very nice.'

'*Bien.*' Pouring some for himself, he leaned back, and, with his long fingers holding the stem, he smiled at her.

'You have dined?'

'Not yet.'

'Then we will dine together,' he said assuredly.

'Will we?'

Amusement danced in his eyes as he nodded. 'I think so. Beautiful women should not be allowed to dine alone.'

'They shouldn't?'

'*Non.* They will be importuned.'

'And you aren't intending to importune?'

'I don't know. The idea has a certain—*charm.*'

She laughed.

'And I dislike to dine alone.'

'So do I,' she agreed softly.

'Then it is a fortunate circumstance, is it not, that I came along when I did?'

'Very fortunate. Did you have a good day's sailing? I assume that's what you've been doing.'

'Excellent. You sail?'

'No,' she replied with a small grin. 'I get sick on a puddle. And I really do think,' she teased softly, 'that Frenchmen should be banned from speaking English.'

'For why?'

'Because the accent is always—devastating.'

'But the man behind the accent—not always, *non*?'

'No,' she agreed.

'And you think that maybe I will be a desperate flirt?'

'I don't know. Are you?'

He gave a slow smile, shook his head. 'I am getting too old for chasing.' Picking up the menus, he handed one to her.

It seemed afterwards that she had done all the talking, that he had skilfully drawn her out, and given very little of himself away. He was amusing, courteous, and wholly delightful. It was gone eleven when the waiter finally lost patience with these lingering diners and pointedly gave Sébastien the bill. He paid it with a smile, added a generous tip, and escorted Gellis to her car.

Standing by the obelisk in the car park, he stared down into her upturned face and smiled. 'You did not bore me once,' he said softly.

'I didn't?'

'Non.'

'And is that unusual?'

'Oui.' Taking her hand, he gently raised it and slowly kissed her fingers. *'A bientôt*, Gellis.'

'Goodnight.'

With a last smile, he released her and walked away. But as she was unlocking the car, a really very silly smile on her face, he halted, walked back.

'Where shall we go tomorrow?'

'Tomorrow?' she echoed stupidly.

'Mmm.'

'I don't know,' she said helplessly.

'Then I will choose.'

'Yes,' she agreed weakly.

He smiled, rearranged his sweater more firmly on his shoulder and walked away again.

'But where shall we meet?' she called urgently.

'Where we met this morning, of course.' He raised a languid hand and was gone.

If it had been in a film, depending on one's point of view, the entire evening would either have seemed absurd or wonderful. He was the sort of man who made women feel special. Certainly he made this woman feel special. Driving back to her apartment near the hospital, silly smile still in place, she gave a soft laugh. And she had wondered whether she would enjoy holidaying on her own?

A door closed nearby—next door, she thought—and she snapped open her eyes. How long had she been daydreaming? Too long. With a deep sigh, a pain in her heart she didn't think would ever go away, she whispered sadly, 'Goodbye, Sébastien.'

CHAPTER SIX

AFTER carrying her case into the lounge, Gellis quickly scribbled Nathalie's phone number on a piece of paper and left it propped on the mantelpiece. Glancing round, she tried to make sure she hadn't forgotten anything—because she wouldn't be coming back, would she? It was four months since she had seen him, but not four months since she had been in this apartment. She hadn't told him that bit. *Couldn't* have told him that, because then he would have known, could have checked.

Staring at the sofa, the sofa she'd sentimentally refused to get rid of because it was where they had first made love, she wondered how different things might have been if she hadn't come back with him that night...

'Are you spending the night?' he asked softly.

Alarm must have flickered in her eyes; it certainly felt as though it had—and excitement, too.

He smiled. 'There's a spare room.'

'Oh.'

'But the temptation would be great. And we mustn't be tempted, n'est-ce pas?'

'No,' she agreed without any clear idea what she was agreeing.

'You wish for me to see if your clothes are dry?'

Did she?

He smiled again, devilish amusement dancing in his

eyes, and traced one long finger across her mouth. 'You see how accommodating I am?'

Not really listening, only wanting, she parted her mouth, gently bit his finger.

'Dangereux,' he warned mockingly. As though in agreement, thunder rumbled menacingly in the distance, and the wind, not to be outdone, renewed its efforts to blow the house down, hurled the rain spitefully at the windows. And Sébastien smiled, moved his mouth close to hers. 'Too late, too late,' he murmured softly. 'You can't go home in this.'

'No,' she agreed. 'Sébastien?'

'Mmm?' he answered absently as he touched his mouth to the corner of hers.

Breathing agitated, heart beating uncomfortably fast, she persevered. 'Why did you wait two weeks to kiss me?'

He stilled, then continued. 'I didn't want to make complications.' And his mouth moved further, nibbled enticingly at her lips.

'And now you do?' she managed thickly.

'Now I am having a very hard time being good.'

'But I don't want you to be good,' she whispered. 'I know.'

He moved back a fraction, and, eyes that looked too big for her small face fixed on his, she asked hesitantly, 'You don't want this?'

He gave an odd smile. 'Oh, yes, Gellis, I want this. I have wanted this since the first time we dined together.'

'Then why?'

'Because I thought I could walk away. And now I don't think I can. The more I saw of you, the more I wanted you. It is all I have been able to think about for days, weeks. And tonight, in the rain, with your face laughing up at me, I gave in to temptation.'

'Is that so terrible?'

'Not terrible, no. Unwise.'

'Because?'

'Because you look like a lady easy to hurt. There is a—a vulnerability about you, an air of fragility. When I first saw you, I couldn't take my eyes from you—neither could any other male in the immediate vicinity.'

'You had your eyes on your paper!'

'Only when you glanced my way. You have the look of mystery, of—difference. Elegant and fragile, as though great tragedy has touched you, great—moments.'

'Do I?' she asked in astonishment.

'*Oui*. You sat alone—not lonely, not uncomfortable. Amusement was on your mouth, in your lovely eyes as you tried to read the *Midi Libre*. You were mouthing the words to yourself, and each time you understood you would give a little nod of satisfaction. And each time a word defeated you you would frown, contemplate and then look it up in your French dictionary.'

'I was trying to improve my French.'

'I know. It was utterly fascinating to watch you, watch that exquisite mouth. And then there was all that beautiful hair, just waiting to be—touched. Like this,' he murmured throatily as he grasped the coil he had made, held it to his mouth—and then held it aside, stared down at her lovely face and groaned.

He murmured something she didn't understand, and, his eyes transfixed on hers, slowly released her hair and deliberately, and very, very slowly, began to undo the belt of her robe. His robe.

Sucking a sharp breath into her lungs, she just stared at him, waited, then shuddered as warm fingers touched her stomach.

'Oh, Sébastien!' she exclaimed on a rush of breath.

'Yes,' he agreed thickly. 'Oh, Sébastien sounds just right.' Moving his mouth back to hers, just touching, barely touching as his warm hand began to rove across her nakedness, he murmured, 'I want to look at you. All of you—touch you, kiss you, hold you. I want your nakedness and your passion… Do you have passion for me, Gellis?'

'Yes,' she managed in a voice that sounded strangled.

'Yes,' he agreed. 'That is why you have been so nervous, isn't it? Because you—want. As I want those beautiful hands to touch me, shape me, feel me. I want… I want so many things from you.'

Breathing out of control, long shudders racking her, she slid her hand beneath his sweatshirt, touched her fingers to his warm flesh, and felt the little jerk he gave.

'Take it off,' she urged thickly.

His abrupt movement nearly tumbling her to the floor, he jerked upright, yanked his sweatshirt off and tossed it over the back of the sofa. Turning back, he parted her robe and slowly brought his chest to hers. Flesh on flesh, warm, exciting—electrifying. He grasped her hair, a handful in each hand, held her head steady, and began to kiss her as no man had ever, *ever* kissed her before.

There was a controlled urgency about him, a passionate need, and it was all the encouragement Gellis needed. *This* was what she wanted. For days, weeks past, *this* was what she had needed. Hands trapped at her sides, she forced them between their bodies, fumbled with and undid the catch on his trousers, undid the zip, discovered with another snatched breath that he was wearing nothing underneath them, and began to ease the material free.

Mouth still clamped to hers, he raised the lower half of his body to accommodate her movements, then wriggled free of the restrictive clothing, kicked the trousers from his feet and lowered his aroused body back to hers. Her gasp echoed his as she wrapped her arms round him, held him tight, kissed him back as though drugged, as though there was all the time in the world to revel in this pleasure.

There were no coherent thoughts, no plans, no awkwardness—just a coming together as though they had been making slow, glorious love to each other all their lives. They moved as one, loved as one, in languor and delight. Sensitised, hypnotised, mesmerised. He would move, she would counter, he would groan and she would echo it. There was no pain, only pleasure, and a brief, shared explosion of laughter as they tumbled to the floor, narrowly missing the coffee-table and the two mugs of cold coffee it still held.

Lying on top of him, hair curtaining either side of her face, she gave a slow, and so very amused, extraordinarily beautiful smile. There was no embarrassment as she stared down into hazel eyes filled with mischief. One of his feet still rested on the sofa, one of her hands was grasping a cushion, a futile attempt to save them from injury. Still joined, exquisitely fulfilled, they both laughed.

'*Vive la différence?*' he grinned.

'*Oui.*'

Slowly untangling themselves, an experience almost as enjoyable as making love had been, they climbed back onto the sofa. He snuggled the robe round her and, still holding the lapels in his strong hands, kissed her gently on the mouth.

'Exquisite,' he murmured, the laughter still in his eyes.

'*Profoundly* exquisite.'

'Let's go to bed.'

She smiled, with her mouth and with her eyes, kissed his mouth as he had kissed hers. 'Let's.'

'I thought I could walk away.' Yes, he had said that. As eventually he had. And yet she couldn't regret what had happened. Having met him, the rest had been inevitable.

And now she must leave.

She didn't say goodbye to anyone. Couldn't bear to. Not wanting anyone to see the pain in her eyes, the sadness, she drove slowly out of Collioure without looking back.

She did not know that Sébastien watched her go. Did not know that he returned to their apartment, wandered round the quiet rooms before he, too, finally left.

She drove mechanically, her mind on Sébastien. Somewhere over the past couple of days she had stopped noticing his harshness, dismissed the memory of how he had been in Portsmouth. He had become, quite simply, her Sébastien once again, and she wanted to go back. And couldn't.

Apart from other very important considerations, her parents were due to go away on the world trip they'd been planning and saving for ever since she'd been a little girl. Sébastien had robbed them of a son-in-law they'd adored; she couldn't allow him to rob them of their dream. But it was hard to drive away from him. Perhaps the hardest thing she'd ever done.

When it got dark, she pulled off the motorway and spent the night in a Novotel. She ate in a nearby restaurant, and then went to her room and stayed there, just lying on the bed, staring at the ceiling, feeling empty and drained. It would have been better if they'd never met again. Then her mind wouldn't be filled with these if only's.

By four o'clock the next day, she'd arrived at Le Shuttle terminal without any clear memory of the journey. She bought a ticket and sat and listlessly waited for the train. Everything seemed unreal, distant. Unaware of the glances she received, the speculation, she saw only inward. How long would it take, she wondered, to forget him? For the hurt to diminish?

Tired, achy, she drove to Portsmouth and pulled thoughtfully into her parents' drive. She would stay the night, wish them *bon voyage* and then she would go home. Home to her little cottage in Hythe, near Folkestone.

But first she would go and see her son. With a smile of anticipation, she hurried inside.

A week later, ten days before Christmas Eve, her parents gone, Gellis settled back in her own cottage; it was as though she'd never been away. Gently drawing back the bedroom curtain so as not to wake the baby, she stared at the distant sea. She spent a lot of her time staring at that sea, imagining Sébastien on the other side. Somewhere. And now it was harder, because his image was clearer. The memory newer.

Should she have told him they were married? That he had a son? Allowed him back into her life? It felt as though she should have. And she had wanted to. So very much. But it would have been pretending. His behaviour would always be between them.

And if she had learned anything over the last few lonely months it was caution. She'd thrown her cap over the windmill once. She couldn't afford to do so again. If she hadn't had a child to think of, perhaps. But she did have a child—and he needed her in one piece.

Her sigh deep, despairing, she stared down into the street, then gave a faint smile as she saw a black dog rummaging in Mrs Nater's dustbin opposite. Perhaps she ought to warn him of the trouble he'd be in if she caught him. She'd only lived in the village a few months, but she knew enough to know what her neighbour was like.

Quite unaware that she herself was also an endless topic of conversation—that people were dying to know who she was, where she had come from, who the baby's father was and *where* he was—she moved about her daily life with an air of unreality. And, despite all that Sébastien had done, she still ached for him constantly, yearned for his touch, his smile. Not a day went by without her thinking of him.

Gently closing the curtain, she went downstairs to make herself something to eat and finish off the cushion covers she was making for the postmistress.

The first postcard from her parents arrived the next day from Madeira, and Gellis gave a wry smile. Perhaps she should have gone with them—at least she would have been warm. At the moment an arctic wind was blowing round the cottage, bringing with it the threat of snow. And the village was readying itself for Christmas. Trees and lights appeared in windows, garlands appeared on front doors. But not her front door.

Kneeling on the lounge floor playing with her son, she watched the snow fall. Small flakes, tiny as yet, and they dusted the fields and roofs like icing sugar. A white Christmas? Maybe. Last Christmas, in France, it had been mild—and they had made so many plans. Had laughed and loved. But this Christmas…? This Christmas would be—lonely.

Looking down at little Sébastien as he enthusiastically whacked the mobile she was holding above him, so much love in her heart for this little scrap, this small part of her husband, she gave a sad smile. Would he ever know his father? And, if he did know, what would he think? Feel? Would he be angry? Sad? And then she smiled as his eyelids began to close.

'You use up my time, little one,' she said softly. 'I spend more time playing with you than doing things I *should* be doing. But we don't care, do we?' Putting down the mobile, she picked him up, held his warm, chubby body against her, nuzzled his soft neck. 'You're getting heavy, my friend.'

Getting awkwardly to her feet, she walked slowly across to the carry-cot and laid him gently down. 'I love you,' she whispered as she covered him warmly up. 'And next year—next year, when you're older, more able to understand, perhaps things will be different.' She might have met someone else. Be married, even. But she couldn't imagine being married to anyone but Sébastien. But next year would be—better.

With a deep sigh, she wandered into the kitchen and stared round her. You're becoming a slut, Gellis, she admonished herself. You never used to leave your kitchen in such a state. Having a baby doesn't mean you have to live in a *mess*, as her mother would have said. With a small grin, she set about clearing up.

Tugging on rubber gloves, she set to work. And half an hour later, face flushed from her exertions, she carried the empty milk bottles to the front door. Putting them on the step, she straightened, stared out at the swirling snow—and caught sight of a tall figure standing on the other side of the road.

'No,' she denied faintly.

Heart thumping painfully, rooted to the spot, her hand groped for and found the doorframe, gripped it tight. He wore no coat, just a thick navy sweater and cords. His hands were shoved into his pockets, and his dark hair was dusted with snow. He looked as grim, as harsh as he had in Portsmouth.

As though in a dream sequence, she watched him walk towards her. Eyes never once leaving hers, he pushed open the gate, closed it meticulously behind him, trod slowly up the path.

'Hello, Gellis,' he greeted quietly, flatly. 'Or should I say Madame Fourcard?'

'What?' she whispered.

'It *is* Madam Fourcard, isn't it?'

Hardening her heart, her mind, she straightened and took a deep breath. 'Yes,' she agreed.

'So why didn't you tell me?'

Defiant, aching, she said, 'I didn't want you to know. Please go away.'

'No. Don't you want to know how I found out?'

She frantically shook her head, tried to edge the door closed. He put his foot in the way.

'I went to your parents' house, and a neighbour kindly told me that they were away. She also told me,' he continued grimly, 'that she had enjoyed my wedding.'

Looking quickly down, Gellis said nothing. There was nothing she could say.

'So what else haven't you told me?' he enquired rather menacingly.

With a frightened little sound in the back of her throat, she tried to slam the door.

He grabbed it, stepped inside and closed it behind him. 'What else? What *else*, Gellis?'

Staring into deep hazel eyes, shaking, mesmerised, assuming the neighbour had told him it all, she whispered, 'That you have a son.'

CHAPTER SEVEN

'WHAT?'

'What?' Gellis echoed in bewilderment.

'What did you just say?' Sébastien demanded hoarsely.

'That you have a son,' she whispered. Eyes wide, too dark, frightened, she took a step back.

'A *son*?' he demanded incredulously. Deep in shock, numb, he repeated blankly, 'A *son*?'

'Yes. I have to—' And, as though on cue, there was a faint cry, followed by a shout, then a wail of temper. With a helpless gesture towards the sounds, she turned away, hurried into the lounge. Her legs felt as though they were made of elastic. Barely able to think, aware only that Sébastien had followed her, that his footsteps sounded heavy, menacing, she walked across to the cot. Picking up her noisy son—their son—she held him protectively against her.

'Shh, shh,' she soothed automatically. 'It's all right, I'm here. He's hungry,' she murmured indistinctly, her back still turned to Sébastien.

'How long?' he asked dazedly. 'I mean, how old is…?'

'He,' she put in. Her voice thicker, realisation beginning to dispel the numbness, she added, 'A little over four months.'

'Four *months*? Did I…?'

'Know? Yes.'

'And what did you…?'

How to play

and claim as many as
FIVE FREE GIFTS:

1. With a coin, carefully scratch away the gold boxes opposite. Then check the Super Bingo Claim Chart to see how many FREE GIFTS you can claim.

2. Send back this card and you'll receive specially selected Mills & Boon® romances from the Enchanted™ series. These books are yours to keep absolutely FREE.

3. There's no catch. You're under no obligation to buy anything. We charge you nothing for your first shipment. And you don't have to make a minimum number of purchases - not even one!

4. The fact is, thousands of readers enjoy receiving books by mail from the Reader Service™. They like the convenience of home delivery and they like getting the best new romance novels at least a month before they are available in the shops. And of course postage and packing is completely FREE!

5. We hope that after receiving your free books you'll want to remain a subscriber. But the choice is yours - to continue or cancel, anytime at all! So why not accept our no risk invitation. You'll be glad you did!

YOURS FREE WHEN YOU MATCH 5 NUMBERS!

You'll look like a million dollars when you wear this lovely necklace! Its cobra-link chain is a generous 18" long, and the beautiful puffed heart pendant will add the finishing touch to any outfit!

Play
⭐SUPER⭐BINGO !...

Scratch away the gold boxes above to reveal your five lucky numbers and see how many match your bingo card. Then simply check the claim chart below to see how many FREE gifts we have for you!

SUPER BINGO CLAIM CHART	
Match **5** numbers	**WORTH 4 FREE BOOKS** **PLUS A PUFFED HEART NECKLACE**
Match **4** numbers	**WORTH 4 FREE BOOKS**
Match **3** numbers	**WORTH 3 FREE BOOKS**
Match **2** numbers	**WORTH 2 FREE BOOKS**

YES! I have scratched off the gold boxes above. Please send me all the gifts for which I qualify. I understand that I am under no obligation to purchase any books, as explained on the opposite page. I am over 18 years of age.

N7LI

MS/MRS/MISS/MR

BLOCK CAPITALS PLEASE

ADDRESS

POSTCODE

THE READER SERVICE: HERE'S HOW IT WORKS

Accepting free books and gifts places you under no obligation to buy anything. You may keep the books and gift and return the despatch note marked 'cancel'. If we don't hear from you, about a month later we will send you 6 brand new books and invoice you for just £2.20* each. That's the complete price - there is no extra charge for postage and packing. You may cancel at any time, otherwise every month we'll send you 6 more books, which you may either purchase or return - the choice is yours.

*Prices subject to change without notice.

The Reader Service™
FREEPOST CN 81
Croydon
Surrey
CR9 3WZ

NO
STAMP
NEEDED

'Call him?' she asked raggedly. 'Sébastien. I'm sorry. I didn't know how to tell you. Didn't know if I *should*. No,' she corrected honestly. 'Didn't *want* to tell you.'

'In case I wanted to come—home?' he asked bleakly.

'Yes.' A rather defiant look on her face, she turned towards him. 'He wants his lunch.'

'Yes. I don't know what to say. I don't, can't—comprehend. Dear God, Gellis, a *son*?' Gripping the back of the chair beside him, he stared at the carry-cot, the blankets tumbled inside, the blue quilt. Then slowly he stared at the small child in her arms. Raising his eyes to hers, he searched her face. 'Don't look like that... *Mon Dieu*, don't look like that.'

Glancing down as the baby squirmed, began protesting, not even sure *how* she was looking, Gellis repeated stupidly, 'I have to feed him.'

'Yes.'

'Do you...? I mean, I have to... Oh, Sébastien, I'm sorry,' she cried helplessly. 'But what else could I do?'

'I don't know.' With a grim laugh, still sounding stunned, he said, 'I came here expecting I don't know what. I was angry, disbelieving, and now... Dear God. A son.'

'Yes.' Not knowing what else to say, she walked into the kitchen, began awkwardly measuring out the milk. Aware that he had followed her, that he was standing behind her, she put the milk in the microwave to heat, got out the baby's dish and put a rusk inside. She found his spoon and bib. And the silence was getting longer, more fraught; even the baby was silent.

Switching off the microwave, she removed the milk.

'Here, let me take him whilst you do that.'

Hesitating, she glanced at him, and he exploded softly, 'I'm not going to *kidnap* him, for goodness' sake.'

'I know. Sorry.'

Accepting the baby from her, he held him awkwardly for a moment, stared down into a curious little face, at the dusting of dark hair and big brown eyes. 'Oh, God!' he exclaimed helplessly. Moving the baby into a more comfortable position, he looked at his wife. 'I can't... Don't know...'

'I know,' she agreed. Pouring some of the milk onto the rusk, she slowly mashed it. Screwing the top on the bottle, she put it into a jug of cold water to cool. Pulling out a kitchen chair, she sat down, held her arms out for the baby. And, like a man in a dream, he slowly handed him over, stood watching whilst she fitted the bib round his neck and began to feed him. And when the dish was empty she wiped the baby's mouth, stood, collected the bottle, and led the way into the lounge.

Still shaking, with no idea of what to say, she sat in an easy chair. After testing the milk on her wrist, she put the teat into the baby's waiting mouth. And what had always felt so natural now felt awkward, unfamiliar. Staring fixedly at the bottle, aware on the periphery of her vision that Sébastien had moved to stand opposite, she determinedly focused on the baby's curled fist and shakily touched it until the chubby fingers curled round her own. Sébastien was here, she had to keep telling herself. He was *here*.

'You said I knew?' he asked bleakly. 'Before I had the accident?'

'Yes.'

'And I *left* you, knowing that I had a child? Had an affair with…?'

'Yes.'

Collapsing bonelessly onto the edge of the sofa, he stared at her in shocked disbelief. 'Dear God.' Searching her face, he waited until she looked at him. 'Why don't you hate me?'

She gave a twisted smile. 'I don't know. I tried to.'

'Was he planned, Gellis?'

'No. An adorable accident. I'd been ill, taken some antibiotics and didn't realise that they can make the pill ineffective. You didn't want children,' she added matter-of-factly, 'and so I thought perhaps that was why you left—that you didn't want the responsibility—and yet…'

'Yes?'

'You were so perfect with him. So—loving.'

'*Mon Dieu,*' he sighed. And after a few moments he asked anxiously, 'Did I make financial arrangements for you and the baby?'

She hesitated, then shook her head.

With an abrupt movement, he got to his feet, went to stand at the window, his back to the room. She stared at him, examined him, felt so unutterably sorry for him.

'Was I there when you had the baby?'

'Yes. You delivered him.'

Swinging round, he demanded blankly, 'I *what*?'

'Delivered him. He was early—and quick. We didn't have time to get to the hospital.'

Shifting the baby into a more comfortable position,

she gave a faint smile at his protest, looked up to share it with Sébastien, and found him looking so anguished that she gasped.

'Oh, Sébastien, don't,' she pleaded.

'I feel—cheated,' he said bleakly. 'How was I? Useless?'

'No. You were brilliant. And you seemed so pleased, so proud...'

'And now I don't remember,' he said heavily. 'Moments like that must have been so special, so cherished; I could weep. *Why?"* he burst out. 'Why in God's name would I have left you? Had an affair with someone else? Asked her to *marry* me when I was already married to you?'

'I don't know,' Gellis stated helplessly.

'Was I impatient with him? Angry?'

'No. You would always get up when he needed feeding, bring him to me...' Lie beside them on the bed.

'How old was he when I left?'

'Three weeks. I'm sorry if you feel cheated, but *I* felt cheated, and so it seemed best not to tell you. I didn't know how you would feel. If you would *want* to know. And you seemed so different. Harsh.'

'Yes,' he agreed quietly.

Watching him, waiting, she asked quietly, 'Why did you come?'

'Because I couldn't stay away,' he said simply. 'I went to Provence, where I had the restaurants. And I saw Nathalie.'

Gellis stiffened slightly, then forced herself to relax. 'And?'

'And she told me what you had told me—that I'd asked her to marry me. That she hadn't known about you and the baby. That we were happy, in love—and that we'd met before. Were in love before.'

'Before?' she whispered.

'Yes. In Provence, before I met you.' With a very unhumorous laugh, he continued, 'And without warning, without notice, I sold my restaurants without telling her and left. And I sent her a note,' he added quietly. 'Do you still have the one I sent you?'

Glancing up at him and then away, she nodded. It was now crumpled and dog-eared from constant readings as she had tried to find a different meaning in the terse message. But it had always come out the same. That he would not be back.

'May I see it?'

She nodded. 'I'll get it when I've fed Sébastien. Did you like her?' she forced herself to ask. 'Nathalie?'

He gave a grim smile. 'No.'

'Because?'

'I don't know. I found her hard, aggressive—flirtatious.' He frowned. 'Coquettish.' Glancing at her hands, at the gold wedding band, he said softly, 'You weren't wearing a ring in France.'

'No. I took it off before we went.'

'But you do *normally* wear it?'

'Yes,' she agreed with a trace of defiance.

He sighed. 'Gérard must have known I was married,' he said quietly. 'He being my lawyer, I surely must have told him. So why didn't he…?'

'Because I asked him not to.' Looking at his set face, then quickly away, she added, 'I rang him when I rang the agent before we went to France.'

'And the people in Collioure? Our friends?'

'They didn't know. Or about the baby. We were

married here, and then we travelled for a while, leased an apartment in Brittany.'

'Which is where you had the baby?'

'Yes. Gérard has the clothing you left there, and your bank statements from January. And I'm surprised that Nathalie didn't tell you you were married and had a son.'

'Are you? I don't think I'm any longer surprised at anything. When were we married?'

'January.'

'So you were pregnant then…?'

'Yes. But I didn't know.' Flicking her eyes to his, she added quietly, 'That wasn't why we got married.'

'*Non,*' he agreed heavily.

Glancing down, she gave a faint smile when she saw little Sébastien staring at her with crossed eyes. Removing the bottle and setting it on the floor, she sat him upright on her knee and began to rub his back. 'Wind,' she explained awkwardly.

'Yes.'

'Would you like…?'

'Like?' His sigh deeper, ragged, he came to perch on the arm of her chair. Reaching out, he took the baby from her, held him as she had done, gently continued to rub his back. His rough hands made little scratchy noises as they caught on the soft wool of the jacket. He looked awkward, unsure. Endearing.

His eyes were on the baby, and so Gellis was finally able to watch him, examine his face at her leisure. It didn't seem so harsh, she decided, but still unfamiliar. Stern. He looked older, a wealth of experience in that strong face. He also looked unbearably sad, and she felt her eyes fill with tears. His thick hair had been trimmed since the last time she'd seen him, and there was a scar on his right cheekbone that hadn't been there before.

And as she stared at him—at that straight nose, that passionate mouth, the long, dark lashes that hid his beautiful eyes—she felt her heart turn over. Wanted to reach out, brush that lock of hair off his forehead, let her fingers linger on his cheek.

He looked up suddenly, caught her staring, and she couldn't look away.

'I couldn't stop thinking about you...' he began thickly—and the baby gave a soft burp. He looked down, smiled. A smile that nearly broke her heart.

Extending one finger, he touched the baby's cheek, then drew it back as though afraid to touch.

'He looks like you, don't you think?' she asked softly.

'Looks like me?' he queried in surprise, then gave that funny twisted grin that always looked so very French. *'C'est possible,'* he shrugged. 'He is my— son. Dear God, but I'm having difficulty absorbing that. It was hard enough when I found out you were my wife, but this...'

'Yes,' she agreed inadequately, and, not knowing what else to say, she murmured foolishly. 'I expect he needs changing.' Getting to her feet, she picked up the nearly empty bottle, handed it to Sébastien. 'He might want to finish it. I'll get his bits.'

Collecting the rubber changing cushion, she tossed it onto the floor by his feet. Still shaking, feeling shivery, *disbelieving*, she collected the baby box and knelt, watched her husband awkwardly give his son the last of his bottle.

Holding out her hands, she took the baby from him and laid him on the mat. He gurgled, waved his arms and kicked, and she gently tickled his tummy. And for a moment as she stared at him she pictured him toddling, going to school, growing into a sturdy young man—who looked so very much like his father. As his father had been.

A lump in her throat, she swallowed hard, and, so very aware of Sébastien watching, gently stripped off the baby's leggings and dirty nappy. She cleaned him, changed him and handed him back to his father. Putting away the mat and the box, she disposed of the dirty nappy, then asked hesitantly, 'Would you like to get him back to sleep?'

Sébastien didn't look surprised, or grateful; he just nodded, and moved to sit in the chair, his son cradled in his arms. He looked so big, so tough, his son so small—and she couldn't believe her husband was there. That he had come back. But for how long?

'If you could put him in his cot upstairs…? He sleeps longer in the afternoons…more comfortable.' Wavering, inarticulate, she murmured, 'I'll go and make some coffee.'

Hurrying away, holding the picture of them together in her mind, she went into the kitchen. And then she began to shake. She clutched the work surface for support and began to shake. He had every right to be angry, but he wasn't—or didn't seem to be. Just anguished.

Grabbing the percolator, trying so very hard not to think, plan, speculate, she filled it, set it to boil, and remembered that she hadn't told Sébastien to lay the baby on his back when he fell asleep.

Walking silently upstairs, she peeped into the bedroom and saw Sébastien standing beside the cot. He was staring down at his sleeping son, so much *pain* etched on his strong face, so much sorrow. The baby was on his back, tucked warmly in, so there was no need for her to go in and speak. Feeling like an intruder, she silently retreated, anguish of a different sort etched on her lovely face.

As she reached the bottom of the staircase, someone knocked at the door. With a tiny sigh, she went to answer it, and found a smile for the health visitor.

'Forget something?'

'Yes. Sorry, Gellis, but did I leave my pen when I was here earlier?'

'Your pen?' Gellis frowned. 'No—at least, I haven't seen it.'

'I think I left it in the kitchen. Do you mind if I look?'

Aware that she was sounding less than welcoming, Gellis forced another smile. 'No, of course not.' Holding the door wide, Gellis invited her in.

'Is that coffee I sme—?' Breaking off, her eyes widened as she saw Sébastien walk slowly down the stairs. 'Oh, my,' she said under her breath.

Gellis also turned to look, saw him as Theresa would see him. Tall, tanned, fit, remote—and so extraordinarily attractive. The sort of man who made the knees go weak, the heart race. Sensuous. Confident. Tougher than when she had first known him, but still utterly devastating. Perhaps more so, because experience had stamped maturity on his strong face— made it stronger.

He nodded to the health visitor, gave Gellis a small smile, and announced abruptly, 'I have to go out for a while. I'll be about an hour.'

'All right,' she said quietly. 'He's asleep?'

'Oui.' He gave another nod to Theresa and left.

'Oh, my,' Theresa said again. She sounded stunned. Staring at the front door as though she could see through wood, she asked blankly, 'Was that…?'

'My husband, yes.'

'He looks—dangerous.' With a little blink, and then a grimace as she realised she'd probably been rude, she turned back to Gellis with an apologetic smile. 'Sorry, but never in a million years would I have pictured your husband looking like *that*! I mean he's…he doesn't look as though… And you're so gentle! Fragile!'

'I'm not in the least fragile,' Gellis denied. 'Come and look for your pen.'

'Right. Yes.' Still sounding stunned, Theresa walked ahead of Gellis towards the kitchen.

And that, Gellis thought wryly, will be all around the village like wildfire. 'Have you seen Gellis's husband? My God, he looks—dangerous'. And so he did. And what did they think her husband *would* look like? she wondered in amusement. Someone gentle, presumably. Which he had been, of course. And funny, and charming and—exciting. But she didn't care what anyone thought. What she cared about was—what happened next?

Gellis fielded the health visitor's questions as she made a token search for her pen, reluctantly poured her a coffee when she asked if she might have one, and began to suspect that Theresa had come because she'd seen Sébastien arrive. Or someone had.

'Your coffee always tastes better than anyone else's,' Theresa murmured as she sipped appreciatively. 'He's big, isn't he?' she added casually.

'The baby?' Gellis asked, being deliberately obtuse.

'No, your husband.'

With the flicker of a smile, Gellis nodded. 'Six foot three. But then I'm a tall girl.'

'Yes. Sexy accent. He's French, isn't he?'

'Yes.'

'And where did you say it was he'd been?'

'I didn't.'

'Oh.' Staring at Gellis's bland face, she suddenly grinned. 'Mind my own business?'

'Mmm.'

'You wouldn't believe the stories that have been going round the village. You're a widow, your husband left you, you weren't married at all. *He* was married…'

'He is,' Gellis said quietly. 'To me.'

'You must have missed him…'

'Yes.'

'And he obviously hasn't been in prison with that tan…'

With a little splutter, Gellis put her cup down and stared at the girl opposite her. 'No,' she agreed firmly. 'He hasn't been in prison. And you didn't lose your pen at all, did you?'

'Yes!'

'No,' Gellis denied gently, and knew she was right when Theresa went pink. 'Don't exaggerate *too* much, will you?'

'What?'

'When you tell the tale.'

'Gellis!'

'Theresa,' Gellis mocked gently.

'Oh, all right,' Theresa agreed. 'I was being nosy. Mrs Markham saw him arrive.'

'And you were elected investigator?'

She grinned. 'Well, you must *know* how everyone's

been speculating! I mean, you arrived out of the blue looking like Sleeping Beauty...'

'Sleeping *Beauty*!' Gellis exclaimed in astonishment.

'Yes,' Theresa said firmly. 'Beautiful, elegant— mysterious. Your eyes so—sad. And whenever anyone spoke to you, asked you anything, you would blink like someone just awakening from sleep, give an enigmatic smile and move on. Of *course* everyone's curious! And, apart from your reserve, you don't *look* like anyone else here. You look—different. Sort of aristocratic.'

'Rubbish! I'm no more aristocratic than you are.'

'No, but you *look* it! And every man over the age of fourteen has been secretly fantasising about you.'

Allowing for exaggeration, Gellis gave a rueful smile and shook her head.

'It's true!'

'Nonsense. And you'd better go and report back before I have someone else knocking on my door wanting to know my business.'

With a shamefaced giggle, Theresa got to her feet. 'At least I gave you time to—greet each other.'

'Yes,' Gellis agreed quietly. Had Theresa imagined passionate embraces? Urgent lovemaking? She wished. Oh, how she wished. And if wishes were horses...

'You aren't angry?'

'No,' Gellis said with a forced smile. 'But I wouldn't try pumping Sébastien if I were you. He's even more uninformative than I am.'

'I wouldn't *dare*! He looks...'

'Dangerous—yes, you said.'

'He also looks—exciting. The sort of man you

might want for a lover.'

'Don't try,' Gellis warned softly.

'No,' Theresa mumbled as she began walking towards the front door. 'I didn't mean— I mean... Oh!' she exclaimed in embarrassed frustration. 'I'll see you later.'

'Mmm.'

'Take care of that baby.'

'I will.'

Thankfully closing the door behind her, Gellis leaned back against it, sighed. Don't try? And what would she do if anyone did try? Nothing—because she no longer had the right. Sébastien didn't remember her. But he had been thinking about her. He'd said so.

A rather bleak light in her eyes, she ran upstairs to quickly shower and change—and then wondered why. She wasn't trying to attract him, because that would be foolish beyond belief. But she did want him. Wanted him so much her heart ached with the intensity of it. But she couldn't have him—mustn't have him—because if he got his memory back... But what was going to *happen* now that he knew about the baby?

Brushing out her long hair, she stared at herself in the mirror. Saw a stranger in a black and white wool dress that buttoned up the front, and low-heeled black shoes. She often wore black and white—had, she corrected, when she'd cared—because it suited her. A small conceit, but now—

Now she didn't know who she was any more, she thought on a surge of panic. It had been such a long time since she'd been in control of herself, her emotions. It was hard to remember how she had been. He'd fallen in love with a laughing girl, but there was no laughter now. Hadn't been for a long time. She tried for a smile, and it looked pathetic, false.

Throwing down the brush, she quickly plaited her hair. A minimum of make-up, a trace of perfume—and a fast-beating heart as she heard his steps on the front path. She knew his walk, the sound of him, and, taking a deep breath in an attempt to still the nerves that were threatening to break out of control, Gellis hurried down to open the front door.

A mass of pink roses obscured Sébastien's face and the most heavenly scent wafted towards her. A teddy sat in the crook of his other arm.

He moved the flowers aside, and said quietly, seriously, 'A little late. I don't remember if I...'

'Yes,' she said quickly. 'You did. Thank you,' she added with a shaky smile as she reached out to take them. 'They're lovely.'

He followed her into the kitchen, sat the teddy on the table. She tried to breathe slowly, evenly, not give in to the tension that racked her, the need to cast herself into his arms. Beg. Staring at the teddy, aware of Sébastien as she had never, ever been aware of anyone else in her life, she saw the label that was hanging round the bear's neck. Putting the flowers down, she reached out to read it. It was in French, and roughly translated, it said, 'Hello, Sébastien. My name is Al Bear.'

With a little smile, Gellis looked up to query, 'Al Bear? As in the French way of saying Albert?'

'Mmm. You've changed.'

'What?'

'Your dress. For me?'

'Yes—no!' she denied in panic. Looking quickly away from the warmth in his eyes, trying to calm the erratic beat of her heart, she stared fixedly at the note, continued to translate.

'I am here to look after you. I will love you and care for you, keep you from harm.'

'Oh, Sébastien,' she whispered.

'Yeah. At least he won't be able to leave without someone taking him, will he? And as far as I'm aware bears don't send notes.'

'No,' she agreed. 'He's delightful.'

'So are you.'

Startled, her eyes flew to his and as quickly away. 'Don't,' she pleaded. 'Please don't.'

'And courageous,' he added as though she hadn't spoken. 'I walked through the town—Folkestone?' he queried, and, when she nodded, continued, 'And I just kept thinking over and over again of how I treated you, of your being all alone. What did you do after I left?'

'Nothing very much,' she said sombrely. 'For the first week I was in shock. I rang Gérard, some of our friends, and no one knew anything, had heard anything. And so I eventually rang my parents. They'd only just gone back,' she added with a bitter laugh. 'They'd been out to see the baby...

'Dad drove to Collioure to see if you'd been back to the apartment. I spoke to the police, anyone I could think of. Gérard drove down—and he was so angry,' she whispered. 'He took all your things back with him, asked if I needed financial help. I stayed a little while longer, just in case, but the rent on the apartment was due, and it seemed silly... So I came here,' she concluded.

He looked grim, unfamiliar. Angry. 'Why didn't

you go back to Portsmouth? At least you would have had friends there.'

'Yes,' she agreed quietly, but didn't explain why she hadn't. That she couldn't have borne anyone's pity. That she'd needed to be on her own with the baby. Needed to—cope. 'I just wanted to shut the world away, I think.'

'Understandable. And I have to keep telling myself I have a son. That he's mine, and I can't... It's so hard, Gellis—' Breaking off, he made an odd little gesture with his hand. 'I can't alter anything, change the fact that I walked out on you—can't pretend that none of it happened. But I am sorry—more sorry than you will ever know. Sorry for hurting you, sorry for—'

'Oh, please don't,' she broke in, distressed. Eyes fixed on his, so much longing in them for everything to be all right, she pleaded, 'Don't let's harp on the past. It can't be changed, and talking about it won't...'

'No,' he agreed, and she gave a grateful smile.

'I expect you're hungry,' she murmured in an attempt to be practical, disperse the tension that had sprung up between them.

'Yes.'

'Would you like...?'

'To stay for a meal?'

'Yes,' she said throatily. 'If you want... I mean...'

'I do.'

Staring down, not wanting him to see the yearning in her eyes, the shaking she was trying so hard to control, she absently stroked the teddy's arm. 'The coffee will be cold. I'll make some fresh.'

He nodded. 'I'll take Al Bear up to Sébastien—if I may?'

'Yes, of course,' she agreed quickly. 'You don't need to ask; I mean—' Breaking off, she gave a helpless sigh.

He gave a grim smile. 'I won't be long.'

With a jerky nod of her own, she turned away to get out another cup, refill the percolator, and let out a shuddery sigh when she heard him leave. Eyes closed, she wrapped her resolution round her like a cloak. He couldn't come back. *Couldn't.* Mustn't. But oh, how she wanted him to.

Shutting it out, not daring to think of it, she stared out at the dark December day—and saw only her own reflection thrown back at her. She hated the winter, hated dark evenings, damp days. She needed sun and warmth, laughter and—love. She missed France. Missed their friends...

With a despairing sigh, she jerked down the blind to shut out the winter day, and turned away to arrange her flowers. Don't think, don't speculate, don't plan, she told herself. Take one day at a time. One hour. One minute.

Carrying the vase of flowers into the lounge, she put it carefully on the sideboard, bent to sniff the scent. It was so hard to be natural, hard to be *articulate* when she didn't know what it was he wanted. Remembering that he had asked to see the note he had sent her, she took it out of the drawer, opened it, read again those few terse lines, then quickly folded it and put it in her pocket when she heard his step on the stairs.

Walking out to the hall, she felt her heart turn over when she saw he was carefully carrying the baby.

'He was awake,' he began defensively, and she grimaced ruefully.

'Trying to make me out to be a liar,' she murmured. Leading the way into the kitchen, she began apologetically, 'I don't have very much for dinner. I haven't been out today.'

He gave a faint smile. 'What *do* you have?'

'Eggs.'

He smiled again. 'Then we will have eggs. Omelette? Gérard's wife said I liked to cook, that I made a very mean omelette. Did I?'

'Yes.' Aware how staccato she sounded, she forced herself to relax. Taking a calming breath, she turned to face him. 'You sound as though you've come to terms with losing your memory.'

Staring down at the baby, he touched his finger to one loosely curled fist. 'I thought I had, until I discovered that not only had I walked out on a wife, but a son as well. I think I've accepted that I probably won't ever get my memory back... Begun to hope I never will. And I'm so very tired of—adventuring. Of not having a purpose in my life. Tired of the—anger.'

Glancing up, he gave a small smile. 'I've been thinking of buying into a boatyard in Port Vendres, opening an art gallery in Collioure. What do you think?'

'Sounds fine,' she said helplessly. 'And you will live there? In Collioure?'

'Probably. Is he all right?' he queried worriedly as the baby began to kick and struggle.

'Mmm,' she agreed as she watched their son. 'He just wants some attention. I'll go and make up the fire, and then...'

'I'll do it.'

With a nod, she took the baby from him and explained, 'The logs and coal are in the garage, through the back door.'

Tucking the shawl more securely round the baby, she sat him on her hip and talked to him as she watched Sébastien go out and return carrying logs, then return for the coal. She listened as he made up the fire—and had to keep telling herself that he must leave.

As he washed his hands at the sink, she studied him, stared at his broad back and wanted to touch. Slide her arms round him, rest her head against him. Be held.

'Why don't you go and put your feet up for half an hour?' he asked as he dried his hands, and began to search for ingredients for the meal.

'I'm all right,' she said quickly. 'I'll just sit here and watch.' And it was nice, comforting, to observe the deft way he prepared everything as she handed the baby a plastic spoon for him to chew on. She watched those long-fingered hands as they peeled potatoes. Hands that had touched her...

'Did you find the note?' he asked quietly.

'Oh, yes.' Taking it from her pocket, she handed it over, watched whilst he read it. It didn't take very long.

Folding it, his face grim, he handed it back.

'He is mine, isn't he?' he asked as he began to whisk the eggs.

'What?'

'The baby. He is *mine*?'

CHAPTER EIGHT

SHOCKED, uncomprehending, Gellis frowned, just stared at him.

'Isn't he?' Sébastien repeated with quiet insistence.

'Well, of course he's yours! Who else's would he be?'

'David's?'

'David?' she queried blankly.

'Yes.' After popping the whisked eggs into the fridge, he poured some fat into the pan and began to heat it.

Forehead furrowed, eyes showing her utter confusion, she repeated stupidly, 'David?'

'Yes. You do know someone called David, don't you?'

'Yes, but I don't understand why... And why on earth would you think...? I mean, who told you about him?'

'Nathalie.' Dropping the sliced potatoes into the pan, he reached for the spatula.

'When?' Gellis demanded. 'When did she tell you?'

'When I saw her in Provence.'

'And *what* did she tell you? And how on earth did Nathalie know about him anyway?'

'I don't know. So who is he?'

'Was,' she murmured absently as she continued to worry about what he was implying.

Carefully removing the pan from the gas, he turned to stare at her. 'Was?'

'Yes. He died a long time ago. Five years before I met you. And you couldn't possibly have thought...'

Now he frowned. 'Five years *before* you met me?'

'Yes. We were engaged. He had a heart attack playing rugby.'

'*Heart* attack? How old was he?'

'Twenty-five. He had a heart defect that no one had picked up on, and one day, playing rugby, he died.'

'*Mon Dieu!*' Sébastien exclaimed in shock. 'And you loved him?'

'Yes,' she said simply. But not as I loved you...

'I see.'

'Do you? What do you see?'

He gave a grim smile. 'I don't know. I thought maybe that was why I left—if I thought... Nathalie said...' With a long sigh, he turned back to the stove. Replacing the pan, he began to turn the potatoes.

'She said,' he continued thoughtfully, but still with that rather grim set to his face, 'that she could understand why I left you. And, when I asked why, she said "Because of David." Said that you were seeing both of us. That when you went to England it wasn't to see your parents but to see David.'

'But how did she *know* about him?' she demanded helplessly.

'I don't know.'

'And I couldn't have been going to see David, because David was dead. And if you'd heard his name mentioned—' she frowned '—you would have asked me. It doesn't make sense, Sébastien.'

'No,' he agreed.

'And is that why you came? To find out?'

'No.'

'No? When you've just accused me of having an—affair? Just accused me of—cheating?'

'No! No, Gellis,' he repeated as he turned to look at her over his shoulder. 'I just needed to—ask.'

'Ask?' she repeated hollowly as she got to her feet. 'You really thought I would try and fob someone else's baby off on you?'

'I don't know,' he stated bleakly. 'I don't know you, do I?'

Staring at him, angry and hurt and bewildered, she shook her head. 'No,' she agreed heavily.

'I didn't know we were married, didn't know I had a son when Nathalie told me about David. But now I *do* know, and I need to know—everything. Otherwise…'

'Something else might leap out of the woodpile?'

'Yes.'

But there wasn't anything else that *she* knew about. Her sigh deep, she glanced down, saw that Sébastien was asleep and gently carried him into the lounge and laid him in his carry-cot. And if Nathalie hadn't told him he might never have come.

Walking slowly back to the kitchen, she faced her husband as he stood where she had left him, spatula in hand, facing the doorway.

'You couldn't have left me because of David,' she said emphatically. 'And I certainly wasn't having an affair with anyone else. I loved you, Sébastien. Loved you more than life itself. I couldn't have cheated. *Couldn't* have. And you should have known that. Not now—because you don't remember—but then… I can't even believe you didn't know about him, that I hadn't told you I'd been engaged before…' With a helpless gesture, she resumed her place at the table.

'Gérard said I was ruthless, but you didn't believe me, did you?'

'No.'

'Rose-coloured glasses, Gellis?' he asked gently.

Had there been? Perhaps.

Turning back to the stove, he poured some fat into the omelette pan and put it on the heat, then bent to remove the mixture from the fridge. 'What happens now, Gellis?'

'I don't know,' she replied.

'And if I never get my memory back? Am I to be denied access to my son?'

She shook her head, realised he couldn't see her, and said quietly, 'No. Now that you know, of course you must have access.' What else could she say? Arms wrapped round her middle for warmth, comfort, she continued to watch him. 'There wasn't a day went by since we met again in Portsmouth without me thinking about it, wondering if I was doing the right thing. But I didn't know you any more, didn't know what to do for the best.'

'No,' he agreed, because he didn't know the answer either. 'Would you like to lay the table? Dinner's nearly ready.'

Nodding, she collected the cutlery and condiments, and, while they ate, mostly in silence, she thought about what was likely to happen next. About what Nathalie had said. She didn't think she would ever forgive the other woman for that. But how had she *known* about David?

Collecting their empty plates when they had finished the meal, Sébastien put them in the sink, made fresh coffee and brought it to the table. 'Travelling here from Provence,' he began quietly, 'everything that had happened, been said by you and Nathalie, kept going round and round in my head. Two women as different as chalk and cheese. And I had left you both. Were there any more, I wondered?'

Searching her face, his own sad, brooding, he demanded helplessly, 'Why? What would make a man behave as I behaved? I don't *feel* like a cheat, a liar.'

'I don't know. Maybe you found the responsibility too much. Maybe you felt restricted, tied. Maybe when you saw Nathalie again in Brittany you realised that you still loved her. I don't know, Sébastien. Do you think I haven't racked my own brains to find a reason? Was it my fault? Did I do something? Say something? Expect too much? I just don't know. Perhaps my pregnancy put you off—me being fat, ungainly—and then when the baby was born perhaps I paid too much attention to him. He wasn't a *good* baby; we didn't get much sleep. We were both tired… Perhaps you felt left out,' she added helplessly.

'But I have a tongue! We surely would have discussed it! Surely there would have been accusations, arguments…?'

'No,' she stated quietly. 'There was nothing. You kissed me goodbye, made sure I had enough money for my immediate needs, had alerted the neighbours that I would be alone for a few days, told me you loved me, that you would be back as soon as you could, and left.'

'Dear God,' he sighed. 'And the note was sent when?'

'Three days later.'

'And Nathalie?'

'Came the day after that.'

Both devoid of further inspiration, they sat nursing their cups, both staring down into the hot liquid, and she sighed again. 'It's getting late,' she murmured.

'Yes. I'd better find a hotel.'

'No! Sorry, I only meant…' Flicking her eyes to his and away again, she gave an embarrassed smile.

'That if I stay in a hotel,' he completed for her, 'everyone will think…?'

'Yes. In a small village everyone knows everyone's business, and—'

'And it's no one's business but our own?'

'Yes. No. I didn't tell anyone that…'

'I'd left you?'

'No.' Feeling awkward, confused, she took a deep breath and asked, 'How long? I mean—'

'How long am I staying?'

'Yes.'

'How long is it permitted, Gellis?'

Glancing up at him, she asked cautiously, 'Permitted?'

'Yes. I have no absolute rights, do I? But he is my son, and I would like to get to know him, find out what he's like, *see* him.'

'Yes, of course.'

Reaching across the table, he took her hands in both of his, absently rubbed his thumbs across the backs of her knuckles, ignoring the rigidity, her attempts to free them.

'Look at me, Gellis.'

Hesitantly raising her eyes to his, she swallowed hard and waited.

'I know you don't want me here, know—'

'Not "want",' she corrected hastily. 'Can't. Can't,' she repeated. 'I *told* you…'

'Yes. Suppose I don't ever get it back, Gellis?'

And she closed her eyes, prayed. 'Don't do this,' she whispered in anguish. 'Don't do this.'

'I must. *Have* to. He's my son. Let me stay for a while, please, get to know him. I've lost my memory, my life. Don't let me lose my son too.'

Oh, that wasn't fair. But true. How could she, in all conscience, send him away? Which, of course, was why she hadn't told him about the baby in the first place.

'You will allow me to stay, Gellis?'

She gave a helpless nod.

'Thank you. And whatever happens I will always make sure that you and the baby are financially secure. You will at least allow me that?'

'Yes.'

'How have you been managing so far? Your parents have been helping you out?'

'No,' she replied quietly. 'The cottage belongs to my uncle. He lets me live here rent-free, and I have some money of my own. Before I met you I used to run a small furnishing business—curtains, quilts, cushions, that sort of thing.'

'And it was lucrative?'

'Yes. Not a shop or anything like that; I worked from home. Commissions,' she added vaguely.

'And now?'

'I made a few quilts when I moved here, curtains…'

'The ones here?'

'Yes. Someone admired them, word got around… I haven't done very much—haven't had the time,' she explained with a flicker of a smile. But she wasn't really paying attention to what she said, listening to what he asked. She was aware only of his touch, and the knowledge that he was staying. The alarming knowledge that they would be sharing the house. A very small house.

'There's only one bedroom,' she blurted out thickly.

CHAPTER NINE

'I CAN use the sofa.'

'It's very short,' Gellis said dubiously.

'I'll manage.'

'It's only a small cottage,' she babbled desperately. 'A bedroom and bathroom upstairs, lounge and kitchen downstairs. I mean, if you'd rather... It's silly to worry what the neighbours will think...'

'But they are your neighbours,' he put in softly. 'And it's your life. Isn't it?'

Wrenching her eyes from his, she nodded. But she didn't want it to be just her life. She wanted it to be theirs. And it couldn't be. Not knowing what else to say, she was relieved when she heard the baby wake.

Withdrawing her hands, she got to her feet and gave a lame smile. After switching on the kettle, she hurried upstairs to collect all the necessary paraphernalia that babies seemed to need.

When she returned, Sébastien was walking up and down, rocking the screaming baby to and fro in his arms.

'Probably knows what's coming next,' Gellis murmured. 'I'll go and, er, get the water for his wash.'

Hurrying into the kitchen, she measured out the milk, mixed it with the boiling water, then poured the remainder of the water into a bowl and carried it carefully back to the lounge. Scolding herself for her stupid nerves, she put it on the floor with the other bits and took the baby from him.

'Nothing wrong with his lungs, is there?' Sébastien said wryly as the baby continued to voice his protest.

'No,' she agreed as she settled him on the floor. 'Hush, hush,' she soothed. 'People will think I'm ill-treating you. He hates being washed and changed,' she explained, feeling constrained to keep talking, explaining. 'And if you think this is bad you should hear him when he has his bath in the mornings. Goodness only knows what the neighbours think. I perhaps should issue them with ear plugs.'

'For sure,' he agreed as he stared with what appeared to be utter fascination at his screaming and very red-faced son. 'You're very competent,' he praised quietly.

'Practice.'

'Yes,' he agreed. 'It must have been very hard,' he commented sombrely. 'Managing on your own.'

'Sometimes, when he was upset or crying and I was tired. But there wasn't a choice, was there? I had to just get on with things, take a day at a time. My parents would have helped more if I had let them—come over, had me over there—but he's my son, Sébastien, and I wanted, needed to take care of him myself. It's easier now that he's older.

'And I might look fragile,' she added with a small smile as she remembered the health visitor's words, 'but I'm really quite tough. And there are an awful lot of women in my position without the cushions that I have. I can work from home, my parents are there if I need them...' It was the nights that were so lonely. Without the warmth and security of a man's arms round her. Looking up, holding his eyes, she said quietly, 'I did the best I could.'

'I wasn't criticising, Gellis.'

'Good. Because whatever the rights and wrongs of it the fact remains that you had an affair with another woman and then left me. I can't forget that, Sébastien. Can't shut it out.'

'No,' he agreed.

'If I had known, if we'd discussed it, if you'd told me that you'd fallen out of love with me, been honest, that would be different, because those things happen. But you didn't. The pain wouldn't have been less, but I would have *known*. Shh, shh,' she added to the baby. 'Soon be done.'

Testing the heat of the water with her fingers, she dumped in some cotton wool. Stripping him off, she was only just in time tossing the end of the towel over him as his little bladder registered an even more violent protest.

'Wretch,' she scolded with a smile.

Glancing up at Sébastien as she quickly washed and changed the baby, she added quietly, 'I'm sorry if that sounds brutal, but I have to be honest. I *can't* forget it, much as I would like to.'

'No,' he said as he watched her fit his son into a sleeping suit.

'I'll go and get his food.' Handing the baby across, she hastened into the kitchen.

His protests stopped mid-wail as he saw what he'd been waiting for, and he beamed at her as though he'd never had a temper tantrum in his entire, short life.

'Yes,' she agreed, 'all for show, wasn't it?' She fitted the bib round his neck and, as Sébastien didn't seem about to give him up, she reluctantly perched on the arm of his chair and began to feed their hungry son.

'You're an absolute piglet,' she scolded gently as

he swallowed the last mouthful in less time than it had taken her to make it. Handing the bowl to Sébastien, she scooped her son up and retreated to the other chair. Picking up the bottle, testing it, she hastily put it in his mouth before he could start yelling again.

Looking up, she gave Sébastien an awkward smile.

He gave a bleak smile back. 'I'll clear this away, shall I?'

'Yes, please.'

Bending, he began to fold the towel, remembered what had happened to it, and bundled it up with the bowl to take into the kitchen. When he came back, he put the cream and packet of cotton wool tidily in the box and closed the lid. And Gellis watched him—the way he moved, touched, was. The way he had done things before he'd left.

'Can I get you anything?'

'What? Oh, sorry. A cup of cocoa?' she asked hopefully, and he pulled a face and went back to the kitchen.

'Made with milk?' he called.

'Yes, please.'

With a funny little sigh, she settled back, stared, mesmerised, at the fire and prayed that she could be strong. Did God listen to desperation?

When Sébastien came back, the tension came with him. He put her cocoa on the coffee-table beside her, then sat opposite and stretched his long legs out before him, ankles crossed. A familiar pose. Dear God, such a familiar pose. And if things had been normal, as they had once been, she would have sat on his lap, baby and all, and fed her son within the secure comfort of her husband's arms. Would probably have still been feeding him herself. But, after Sébastien had left, her milk had dried up. All the stress and anxiety, the doctor had said.

Swallowing the lump in her throat, she looked down at their son, smoothed one hand gently over his dark hair.

'He's beautiful, isn't he?' she said softly.

'Yes. He has your eyes. But it could get a little confusing, us both named Sébastien,' he commented quietly.

'Yes. We called him S.J.—Sébastien Junior.'

'Did we? I wish I could wipe it all away, Gellis. Memory loss sounds so damnably convenient, doesn't it?'

'I don't doubt that you've lost your memory, Sébastien.'

'I know.' With a long sigh, he asked, 'How often do you have to feed him?'

'The same as me, except that he has a last drink before he goes to bed around eleven. He then usually sleeps through until six—usually,' she stressed. 'We're a bit behind today. He woke at four this morning, and so he had a feed he wouldn't normally have had. And then everything else was a bit late,' she added foolishly.

He nodded. 'You do not mind me asking? Only I have a need to know, you see. A curiosity, because these are things I should already know.'

'Yes. Are you angry that I didn't tell you?' she whispered hesitantly.

'Not with you. I just keep thinking that—' Breaking off, he uncrossed his legs and drew them in. Leaning his elbows on his knees, he stared round the small room, at the sewing machine in one corner, at the drapes at the window. 'These are curtains that you made?'

'Yes. And the cushion covers and cushions. Nothing special, just…' Stop babbling, Gellis, she scolded herself—he can't be remotely interested in your domestic arrangements.

'They're very nice. Why don't you have a Christmas tree?'

'Oh, because I—' How to say that, without him, it had all seemed meaningless? 'Haven't had time,' she concluded lamely.

There was another awkward little silence, and then he asked, 'Did we—celebrate Christmas, Gellis?'

'Yes,' she said quietly.

'Tell me. What happened last year? Did we have a tree? Decorations?'

'Yes, you said… It was our first Christmas together,' she remembered quietly as she stared down at their son. 'The tree was enormous…' With a faint smile as she remembered their struggle to get it through the front door, she looked up and her face softened.

'It was a splendid tree, Sébastien. We forced it through the hall, scratching paintwork, stood it in the corner by the window, and you spent an absolute fortune on baubles and tinsel.' As well as an absolute fortune on presents for herself and her parents. 'It was a good time,' she murmured reminiscently, able to see it all so clearly. 'A happy time. Mum and Dad came out. We had so many invitations that Christmas—restaurants, bars—and you invited most of them to join us for Christmas dinner.' She smiled.

'And did they come?'

'Oh, yes. You were very well-liked.'

'And you, Gellis? Weren't you liked too?'

She gave a funny little shrug. 'I suppose.'

'Did I cook the meal?'

'Yes. And carved the turkey. We wore silly hats and drank too much wine. Laughed.'

'And this year there is no tree, no garland on the front door,' he commented softly.

'No.' Returning her eyes to her son, she didn't know what else to say.

'Gellis?'

Hesitantly looking up, she stared into his dear, familiar face and felt her throat block. 'Yes?' she asked huskily.

'We'll get a tree.'

Feeling sad, bereft, afraid to hope, she looked away. Nodded.

Straightening his back, shrugging to ease the tension in his shoulders, he got to his feet. 'I'll go and get my things from the car.'

'Car? You drove over?'

'No, hired one from the airport.'

She nodded, then bit her lip. She hadn't even asked how he had got here. 'And are you still…?'

'Using a false passport? *Non*. I am now legal.'

'Good.'

He smiled, and when he went out she leaned back, thought about what he had said. Why did he want her to have a tree? Because he understood? Even if he didn't remember?

Returning her eyes to the fire, she gave a gentle sigh. Her parents had adored him. They'd all got on so well together—her father had become an expert on wines. Or thought he had, she remembered with a fond smile. He and Sébastien had enthusiastically explored the wine caves, sampled more than one bottle, on more than one occasion... And her mother had become very French. She'd taken to market shopping like one to the manner born. Despite the language barrier, she had entered into vegetable prodding with the best of them.

With a resolute little shake of her head, Gellis forced the tears away. One hour at a time. One minute—because this 'new' Sébastien was very hard to read. He did not act, think, seem to feel as he had before, and so it was difficult to guess what it was he might want. If he was staying only for the baby's sake... It didn't alter the fact that he would be here, though, did it? Didn't alter the fact that she had to cope with her feelings.

And if he hadn't lost his memory? What would he have been doing now? Seducing someone else? She didn't know. She simply did not know. And Nathalie? What was she doing now? And would things have been different if she hadn't come? She didn't know that either.

Staring into the flames, she felt her eyelids begin to droop and snapped herself awake.

When he returned a few minutes later carrying a small holdall, she stared at the rapidly melting snow that frosted his head and shoulders. 'Still snowing?'

'Yes,' he smiled. 'And lying. Tomorrow I could build you a snowman.'

'A snowman?' Eyes searching his, she felt warmth steal into her cheeks. That was a remark that the old Sébastien might have made. She wished she knew what it was he really wanted. With an awkward smile, she looked quickly away. 'I'll find you some blankets in a minute.'

'Thank you.' Putting his bag by the sofa, he returned to his chair.

Did he feel as constrained as she? Awkward? Tense? Had he expected a different response to his remark about the snowman? It wasn't going to be easy, was it? They were different people now. Strangers who needed to learn. And, if there hadn't been a baby, would he have wanted to stay at all? Certainly he hadn't brought very much with him. Judging by the size of the holdall, he just had a change of clothes and underwear. Enough for a weekend.

Glancing down at her son, seeing that he'd finished, she removed the bottle, wiped his mouth—and Sébastien leaned forward, held out his arms.

Leaving him with his son, she carried the baby's things upstairs to the bedroom and found sheets, blankets and a pillow to make up the sofa.

As she went back downstairs, her heart began to thud painfully. Just the thought of walking into a room where he was, just the thought of seeing him, could do this. Taking a deep breath, she walked into the lounge, and halted in the doorway to stare at her husband and her son. Sébastien was staring into the flames much as she had done, the sleeping child held safely over one shoulder, his cheek resting against the baby's. He looked—anguished. Heart aching, she walked across to the sofa, began making up his bed.

'I can do that,' he said quietly, and she halted, nodded.

'All right. Will you make sure the fire is all right before you go to sleep? Put the guard in front?'

'Yes, of course.'

'Then, if you don't mind, I'll go to bed.'

'Yes.'

With another deep breath, she walked across to take the baby from him, and as she bent down her plait fell across his chest, seemed to cling, linger there. They stared at each other for long, long moments, the atmosphere charged. Almost frightened, Gellis scooped the baby from him and quickly straightened.

'Goodnight,' she said huskily.

'Goodnight, Gellis. You wish for me to carry him upstairs for you?' he asked as he got to his feet.

'No,' she denied hurriedly as she backed away from the bulk of him, the nearness. 'Truly, I'm fine. Goodnight.'

Hastily escaping, she walked upstairs and into her room. If she'd allowed him to carry the baby upstairs, he would have been here, in the bedroom. Glancing at the double bed, she gave a troubled sigh. There was such an ache inside her, such a big ache—but there couldn't be, could there? Mustn't be. Supposing he stayed? Supposing it was as it had been before—and then he got his memory back? Remembered why he'd left? And left again? No, she couldn't cope with that. Could not ever cope with that.

She'd left the bedside lamp on to light her way and, dropping a warm kiss on the baby's forehead, she put him to bed. 'Goodnight,' she whispered. 'Sleep tight.'

After making sure he was warmly covered, she moved silently to the window, eased back the curtain and peered out, watched the snowflakes drift past the window. If it got very bad, he wouldn't be *able* to leave, would he? And then what? The tension would build and build as it had in France... And she wanted him. Dear God, how she wanted him.

She replaced the curtain, face troubled, and got ready for bed. She knew she wouldn't sleep. Knew her mind would dwell on him lying or sitting just a few yards away. And as she lay there, staring into the dark room, she kept seeing that moment when her plait had tangled against his sweater—when they had looked at each other—and felt her heart begin to beat just that little bit faster.

She imagined a different ending. Imagined herself leaning closer, could almost feel the touch of his lips on hers. Had he been thinking of it, staring broodingly into the fire? Or had it held no significance for him at all? She wanted to creep downstairs, make sure he was still there. Watch him sleep—and it felt as though she had just drifted off when the baby woke her at six.

Stumbling downstairs, only half-awake, she made his bottle and climbed back up to her room. Picking up S.J., she took him into bed with her. 'Shh, shh, shh; you'll wake the whole street.'

Her eyes closed, and she hazily drifted whilst the baby got on with what was the most important thing in his life. Sébastien knocked softly on the door and came in.

'I heard you get up,' he said quietly. 'I thought you might like a cup of coffee.'

'Thank you.' Aware of her tumbled hair, her sleepy face, she gazed at him helplessly. Unshaven, his sweater and cords hastily pulled on, feet bare, he had never looked more lovable.

'Is it still snowing?'

He smiled, shook his head. 'But everywhere looks beautiful. Crisp and cold and white.' Putting the coffee on the bedside table, he stared at his son. 'Is there anything I can do?'

Yes, she wanted to say—climb in beside me, hold

me as I hold your son. But she couldn't say that, could she? So she shook her head.

'Is it all right to have a shower?'

'Yes, of course. You don't need to ask.'

He gave an odd smile, returned his attention to his son. 'Will you go back to sleep when you've fed him?'

'Oh, no,' she said. 'I'll get up.'

'There's no need. I'm here if anyone knocks or rings. Why don't you have a lie-in? Catch up on your sleep?'

Unsure what to say, what she wanted, she merely smiled. 'Maybe. I'll see. Thank you for the coffee.'

'Don't let it get cold.'

'No.'

We sound like polite strangers, she thought as he went out and quietly closed the door behind him. She felt a lone tear trickle down her cheek and impatiently wiped it away. There was such pain in her heart for him. Such an awful longing, and it must be denied.

She heard him go into the bathroom, heard the shower running, pictured him naked... Feeling hot, uncomfortable, ill, she closed her eyes in defeat. This wouldn't work. Couldn't work.

When she'd fed the baby and put him back in his cot, she set the mobile running to entertain him, then drew aside the curtain to check on the weather. It had obviously been snowing hard in the night, because everywhere was thickly covered in a blanket of white.

Fascinated by the transformation, she gave a slow smile, felt like a child again. Wanted to rush out, make footprints in the virgin covering. Make a snowman. And soon, as people began to go to work, school, that pristine pavement would look scuffed and

spoiled. Already the milk float had left twin tracks
down the centre of the lane, and she gave a soft laugh
as she saw the postman deliberately walk all the way
round Mrs Nater's snow-covered lawn to outline her
flowerbed with his footprints.

Still smiling, she turned away to begin another day.
A day that would be different. Because Sébastien was
here.

At ten-thirty, all immediate chores done, the baby
given his breakfast, Sébastien asked if she wished to
come and help choose the tree.

'Help?' she asked drily.

Head tilted to one side, amusement in his green-
flecked eyes, he asked whimsically, 'Do you by any
chance imply that I am an autocrat when it comes to
tree-choosing?'

Her own eyes mirroring his smile, she nodded,
pursed her lips. 'Mmm, hmm.'

'A slur, I am sure, but I will nevertheless rephrase
the question. Would you like to come and watch *me*
choose a tree?'

With a little grunt of laughter, she nodded again,
then had to look hastily away from the warmth in his
eyes. There was a pain in her chest—hard and tight…

'Then go and get your coat and boots and I will
arrange the pram. We can get a tree in the village?'

'Yes. I like to shop locally if I can. Support the
shopkeepers.'

He nodded. 'As in France. Otherwise, all we will
have is supermarkets.'

'Yes. Village life, in whatever country, should be
preserved.'

'I agree. Go and get your coat.'

Collecting her jacket and winter shoes, she dressed

the baby in his padded suit and put him in the pram that Sébastien had wheeled into the hall from the garage. Covering her son up warmly, she turned to find Sébastien frowning at her.

'Where are your boots?'

'I don't have any. These are fine.'

'No, they are not,' he argued. 'The snow will cover them in seconds. And that jacket is no good. It's cold out, Gellis. Go and get a coat.'

Exasperated, embarrassed, feeling almost *guilty*, for heaven's sake, she said quietly, 'I don't have a coat.'

'Why? You told me you had enough money for your needs!' Face tightening, he added angrily, 'Because if you haven't, if you've been living hand-to-mouth because of me...'

'No! No, it has nothing to do with money. I haven't had time!' Or, if she was honest, the inclination. 'I'll get one whilst we're out,' she promised hastily.

'You can get a coat and boots in the village?'

She shook her head. 'I'll go into Folkestone or Dover when we've bought the tree.'

'We'll go into the town first.' Still staring at her, his face bleak, he said quietly, 'I was a wealthy man. Why would I leave you unprovided for, Gellis? Why? Whatever I might have felt, wanted, needed, why would I leave you without money?'

'Perhaps you knew I had some. Perhaps if you thought the baby wasn't yours— I don't *know*, Sébastien! Shall we go?'

'Yes,' he agreed tightly. 'I can take the hire car back; the company has a branch in Dover. We'll get your shopping, then they can drive us back to the village.'

'They won't do that!'

He looked astonished. 'Of course they will.'

Staring at his resolute face, Gellis gave a mental nod. Yes, they probably would. Even before his accident, if Sébastien wanted something done it usually was. And he looked a great deal more autocratic now than he had then.

'The pram will fold into the boot?'

'Yes.'

He nodded, shrugged into his own thick jacket that must have been in the car, removed the baby from the pram and handed him to Gellis. 'You have a baby seat?'

'In my car.'

He nodded again and wheeled the pram out. Five minutes later, the pram stowed in the boot, the baby seat fitted, Gellis collected her bag and keys, locked the front door behind her and climbed obediently into the back of the car.

After fitting little Sébastien into his seat, she clipped her seat belt in place and stared at the back of her husband's head. His anger wasn't directed at her, she knew that, but it hurt just the same. How must it feel to suddenly find out that you were a rat? Heart aching for both him and herself, she gazed out at the snowy landscape.

The shopping completed—with Gellis wearing her new sheepskin coat and warm boots—they had lunch in Dover, and, when they'd eaten, Sébastien asked if there was a room Gellis could use in which to feed and change the baby. Gellis wasn't in the least surprised to find that they had. Had she been on her own and asked, they would have been sympathetic but regretful. But, because Sébastien asked, one was found.

Still feeling introspective and sad, she settled down

to feed her son whilst her husband went for a look round the ancient town.

When he returned, she saw that he hadn't only been looking. Several large carrier bags were held in one strong hand, but he merely smiled when she asked what he'd been buying.

The hire company took them back to the house, and, when Sébastien had put his bags and the baby seat inside, they walked down to the village. Sébastien pushed the pram. He looked a bit silly—but she had no intention of saying so.

'People will look at you,' she warned him quietly. 'Want to know where you've been.'

He glanced at her sideways, gave a small smile.

'Although Theresa—the health visitor,' she explained, 'decided you probably hadn't been in prison because of your tan.'

His smile widened, and there was a little spark of mischief in his hazel eyes. 'What would the old Sébastien have said?' he queried.

'Something outrageous.'

'Then I will ponder on the outrageous. I think per'aps my English is not good. *Non?*'

'*Non,*' she agreed with a delightful smile of her own, and then she chuckled, shook her head. It was like it had been before. Delightful nonsense. But it *wasn't* as it had been before, she cautioned herself. And never would be again.

'What is it?' he asked quietly, and she forced a smile, shook her head.

Aware that it was becoming more and more difficult to push the pram, she halted him and kicked the snow from the wheels with the toe of her new boot.

'I could have paid for the coat and boots,' she said softly.

'Yes,' he agreed quietly.

'If you hadn't lost your memory, it would be different. But you have, and so you don't need to atone.'

'Yes, Gellis, I do. I also want to be—needed. It's easy now to be generous with money. A pity I wasn't so generous before. Or with my—behaviour. Perhaps then—' Breaking off, he made an odd shrugging gesture.

'Don't,' she put in quickly. 'Let's not talk about that.'

He nodded. 'Where do we go for the tree?'

'Greengrocer's. Just up ahead.'

'And does the greengrocer have—curiosity?'

Slanting him a smile, Gellis nodded.

'Then tuck your hand in my arm. I have been away a long time, and we are…'

Lovers? Overjoyed to be together again?

'…happy to be a couple again,' he finished. But he didn't sound happy. He sounded—sad. Bleak.

And when—if—he got his memory back, and he went away again, what would she tell the villagers then? She had no idea. Perhaps he could work on an oil rig, be an outback explorer… He would presumably come back to visit the baby from time to time…

She spoke with the greengrocer, her voice soft, as it always was. She conferred with Sébastien in French, tried very hard not to giggle, and was quite unsure of the yearning that shone in her eyes when she looked at her husband.

Sébastien paid for the tree—the largest there—chose a great many vegetables, and arranged to collect everything when they had finished the rest of their shopping.

The greengrocer offered to deliver it. It was on his way home, he said.

Sébastien thanked him in deplorable English, and Gellis bit her lip.

'What other shopping?' she asked unsteadily as they left the shop.

'Meat. Your cupboards, Gellis,' he reproved her, 'are bare. The freezer is stocked with ready-made meals, there are no ingredients to make soup—' Switching quickly to French as they passed a knot of women gossiping on the pavement, he smiled at them with great charm, and they parted to let them through with the pram. And one, perhaps braver than the rest, halted their progress so that she could peer in at the baby, and gave Sébastien an arch look. His eyes glinted with amusement, and she blushed, stepped aside.

Gellis smiled at her. It wasn't her fault. Women always found Sébastien attractive. A challenge. When she'd been secure in his love, it hadn't mattered. Now it did. But no one would ever be allowed to know that, and so she smiled at the woman. Pretended that she didn't mind.

Aware of the eyes that followed them as they made their slow progress through the village, she glanced up at her husband and forced another smile.

'Are your ears burning?'

'Red-hot,' he agreed. Halting outside the butcher's, he instructed, 'Wait here; I won't be a moment.'

'I don't think he speaks French,' she warned with a little flash of amusement, and he looked at her from under his lashes.

'My English is improving all the time,' he informed her loftily. 'And, failing that, I can always point.' Disappearing inside, he left Gellis with a little smile on her mouth. Carols were wafting out from several shops, and she stared up at the grey sky, wondered if it would snow again.

Would he be here for Christmas? Would there be presents wrapped beneath their tree? A turkey? She didn't know how to ask, but as they walked slowly back to the house there was a poignancy about it all, an anticipation that wouldn't go away.

The fire was nearly out, and, whilst Sébastien re-kindled it, Gellis put the shopping away. It was just a small domestic scene, enacted all over the country. But this was different. This was pretending.

The tree was duly delivered, put up and decorated with the things Sébastien had bought in Dover. And there was a sadness about it, tension. Whilst they'd been out, with other people around them, it had been easier. But here, alone, with just the baby for company, it was harder. She wanted to touch him, hold him, laugh with him. Wanted to share memories that he no longer had any knowledge of.

They did not talk very much, but she would catch him watching her, as he would catch her watching him, and tension began to simmer between them again, a tension that got worse over the next few hours.

She didn't know if he was tense because he knew how she felt and was afraid she was going to do something, say something that would change everything. She only knew that she couldn't go on like this. Conversations became even more stilted, accidentally touching was a nightmare, and she was becoming forgetful, distracted.

She went to bed that night without knowing how she had got through the day. And, in the morning, not thinking, not looking, she walked into the bathroom—and found Sébastien there, shaving. A towel was knotted round his waist, and his torso was bare.

Frozen in the doorway, eyes haunted, she watched as he scraped the last bit of stubble from his chin and rinsed his razor in the basin, and she gave a despairing little cry that was as unconscious as it was unwanted. He stilled, glanced sharply at her in the steamy mirror, his eyes bright.

'Sorry,' she apologised huskily. 'I forgot. I just came in to get the baby's washing.' Hurrying across the bathroom, eyes averted, she grabbed for the small laundry basket just as he grabbed for the face towel. Their hands touched—and reason splintered.

CHAPTER TEN

WITH another cry, Gellis dropped the basket, closed her eyes tight, and Sébastien's hand gripped her arm. Hard.

'Gellis,' he said thickly, and then he cursed, dropped his razor and dragged her into his arms.

Clutching at him, staring frantically into his eyes, she snatched in a shaky breath and kissed him. She couldn't help it, didn't want to help it. She needed him. As a fish needs water, she needed him.

He didn't push her away, just groaned, held her tighter and kissed her back with the same urgency, the same desperation.

It wasn't gentle, it wasn't lover-like, just pure animal reaction. Desperate hunger. Head bent back, eyes closed, fingers digging into his flesh, she kissed him as though she would never stop. *Could* never stop. As he kissed her.

His body was warm, the flesh firm, taut, and she feverishly began to run her hands over his well-muscled back, his shoulders, into his thick hair to press his head closer, harder, little inarticulate sounds issuing from her throat. Four months she had waited for this. Four *months*!

He moved, turned her so that her hips were against the basin, a barrier to prevent escape as he pressed against her, harder and harder until she could barely breathe. Until all she could feel was the imprint of his body against hers, the hard rim of the basin against her buttocks. Her towelling robe was a roughness she didn't need, couldn't cope with, so she wrenched it aside so that the only thing between them was the thin silk of her pyjama top. And still it was too much. She needed to feel his flesh against hers, against the fullness of her breasts, needed to feel all of him against her. As did he.

With a muffled sound in the back of his throat, he wrenched her robe free, ripped the belt from its loops. But her arms were still clenched round him so he couldn't free her pyjama top entirely—but he could undo the buttons. Just.

Fumbling in his haste, he bared her chest and pressed her against him with a sharp intake of breath. Breathing erratic, still pressing feverish kisses against her mouth, he jerked her pyjama bottoms down, whipped away his towel, and they both shook, trembled as though fevered.

'Gellis…'

'Oh, God, don't stop.'

'No,' he agreed thickly. 'I can't.' Moving his hands to her thick hair, he grabbed it painfully, stared into her flushed face and gave a convulsive shudder.

'I'm sorry,' he apologised as he briefly closed his eyes.

'Don't be. Don't ever be sorry,' she whispered. 'I've wanted this for such a very long time. Such a *very* long time.' Hand trembling, she touched her fingers to his mouth, his cheek, and then to the badger stripe at his temple.

'It won't go away.'

'No. I like it.'

He gave a crooked smile. 'You have shaving foam

on your nose.' As he gently wiped it away with his thumb, his face sobered, darkened.

'I lied,' he husked. 'I didn't stay for the baby's sake. I stayed for yours. I stayed for yours,' he repeated emotively. 'I wanted you. All this time, ever since I saw you in Portsmouth, I've wanted you. You've been haunting me, Gellis, and living in the same house with you, seeing you every minute of every day, knowing that you slept just yards away and I could not touch, was driving me insane. I don't think I've ever been so constantly aroused in my life!'

Words pouring from him, half in French, half in English, kissing her between words, phrases, he continued thickly, 'Your beautiful hands as they changed Sébastien, elegant hands, competent, slow—I imagined them touching me, stripping me...'

'And if S.J. hadn't been here? Would you really have stayed?'

'Yes. I didn't know how I would ask, how I would contrive it...'

'And then you didn't need to?'

'No. But if he hadn't been here I would have found a way. Seeing you again, more beautiful than my memory of you, just a week after you'd left—a horrendous week, torturous—I wanted you, could have taken you there on the front doorstep. I wanted you in France in the same manner, with the same urgency—and I had to let you go. And, even if I get my memory back, I can't, *won't* believe that I could betray you again.'

'No,' she agreed, her voice as rusty as his.

'I couldn't stop thinking about you, wanting you. Gérard said you had a smile that would stop a tank in its tracks, and I had never seen it, could not remember it—and, oh, Gellis, I wanted to. Wanted to know you as you had been. Wanted to see the girl I had fallen in love with. He said I was bewitched by you, besotted, and that the love in your eyes for me made the heart ache. And if I don't remember, can't ever remember, I want to feel it, experience it.'

'I—I can't—smile,' she stuttered unevenly, 'but I can love.' Stiffening suddenly, she groaned, shook her head, clutched him tighter. 'No. I can't. I forgot.'

'Forgot?'

'Yes. I have to go to the doctor's,' she said urgently.

'What? Now?'

'Yes. No. Oh, darling, I can't even think.' Tugging his head back, not wanting to lose the warmth of him, the feel of him, she stared into his face. A dear face. A lovely face. 'After the baby—after you left—I'm not on the pill. I have to get some, and I don't know how long before... Oh, Sébastien.'

'Ring him,' he urged thickly.

'Now?'

'Yes. No. I don't want to let go of you.'

With a shaken smile, she rested her head against his strong shoulder, held him tight. Revelled in the feel of the warm body that fitted so perfectly with her own.

'I don't want to let go of you, either,' she whispered. 'It's been so long.'

Sliding his mouth down her exquisite cheek, he bit gently into her neck, moved to her ear. 'Show me how I loved you,' he urged throatily. 'Show me how it was.'

Feeling shivery and shaky, too warm, she breathed, 'Yes. Oh, yes.'

Scooping her up, he carried her to the bedroom, laid her almost reverently on the bed. Tossing away the pyjama bottoms that had been twisted round her ankles, he lay beside her, pulled her into his arms.

'We can get rid of this, can't we?' he murmured as he tugged at the towelling robe.

'Yes.' Slipping her arms free, she snuggled urgently against him, began to smooth her hand feverishly up and down his body. She touched him where she had longed to touch him for so long, and he shuddered, gripped her tight.

Needing his kisses, his mouth on hers, she arched, stretched her neck so that she could reach, touched her tongue to his lower lip, then rolled to cover him so that she could kiss him properly, feel his warmth all along her length. And if it wasn't what he wanted, if she was being too eager, she no longer cared.

'It was like this?'

'Yes. Not so desperate, perhaps, but yes, this is how it was. Always the need to touch, hold.'

'We could use another form of protection,' he murmured.

'No,' she replied with a shaky laugh. 'I hate them. So do you.'

'Do I?'

'Yes.'

'Then I will think of other ways to make love without risk. Many ways,' he encouraged as he ran his strong hands up and over her long back. 'Not quite as fulfilling as being joined, but delightful nevertheless—satisfying, pleasurable.'

'Yes,' she agreed, as she would have agreed to anything he said just then. Touching his face, his dear face, a face that no longer looked stern, she moved her mouth back to his and their passion accelerated out of control.

Finally, spent, breathing unsteady, they stared into each other's eyes as though both were afraid to look away, as though any hesitancy now, any movement, might break the spell.

'No regrets?' he queried huskily.

She shook her head.

'No second thoughts?'

She shook her head again and her hair slipped over one naked shoulder, slid across his neck.

'Gellis?'

'Yes?' she answered rustily as they continued to stare into each other's eyes.

'I don't want to be anywhere but here.'

'No.'

'Don't want anything but this.'

'No.'

Raising one hand, he gently touched his long fingers to her cheek, her lips, touched one finger incredibly softly against her lashes. 'I would like to hold this moment for all time,' he said in French. Slipping his fingers into her hair, he combed them through the long strands. 'One single moment that will stay with me for the rest of my life. But there are other memories locked away inside my mind, memories I can no longer recall.

'But, if I have learned anything in these last four months, it is that each moment must be savoured, relished. Each moment, each minute—because they can never be lived again. And, even if they can't be remembered, they have been lived. And so I want to savour this, store it against my future dark days, offset it against all the hurt and pain. I need you, Gellis. For this one brief moment in time, I need you. Do you understand what I'm saying?'

'Yes,' she whispered. 'None of us knows what's round the corner, and so we must grasp each moment and make it special. But, oh, Sébastien, I couldn't bear…'

'Shh.' Splaying his fingers against her nape, he drew her slowly towards him until his mouth could brush hers, so that his tongue could touch enticingly against her lips, part them, until, with a little groan, he held her tight, rolled her to lie beneath him. And, in the few hours before the baby woke for his feed, they lay naked on her bed, gently explored each other, stored memories against any future dark days.

He lay inside her whilst she fed little Sébastien, one large hand propping up his own head—watched her, touched her, smoothed his other large hand across the baby's head.

'He's beautiful,' he said thickly.

'Yes. It's nearly lunchtime, and he hasn't had his bath,' she added ruefully, her voice still husky from their lovemaking.

'His mother had more important things to do.'

'Yes.' Glancing at Sébastien, unable to smile for the feelings that filled her up, Gellis's eyes said all that she could not say, and his own eyes darkened with renewed passion.

Voice thick, accented, he murmured, 'How could I have cheated? Left you? How can you be like this after what I did?'

'I love you,' she said simply. 'I always have. Always will. I don't think I can stop, even if I wanted to.'

'I don't want you to.' His hand tightening warmly

on her thigh, he continued throatily, 'Did you never feed him yourself?'

'Yes,' she replied huskily. 'You would lie and watch me, and…'

'I can imagine the ''and'',' he murmured thickly. Bending his head, he touched his tongue to one proud nipple, and groaned. 'I kept—wanted…' With a crooked smile and an endearing shrug, he didn't finish the sentence. He didn't need to. He had only wanted what she had, after all, and as the baby continued to feed Sébastien explored and caressed Gellis's body until she felt sick with longing.

'I don't remember loving you,' he said quietly, 'but I intend to remember it in the future. I won't ever forget this again. Not ever. Go and ring the doctor,' he pleaded urgently. 'I'll look after Sébastien.'

Unable to speak, she nodded, handed baby and bottle across. Reaching for her robe, she went downstairs to ring the surgery. Feeling loved, fulfilled and wanted, hand shaking, she waited for the phone to be answered.

Pushing into the bedroom a few minutes later, she halted, smiled. Still naked, he was kneeling above his laughing son on the bed, teddy held above him. He had a beautiful body—narrow hips, long, shapely legs, a broad back. His dark hair curled enticingly against his neck and Gellis felt desire unfurl inside. Desire and longing.

He might not remember her, remember their marriage—he might have hurt her. But right at this moment she would change nothing. They would build new memories, and in time… Perhaps in time, if she were patient, he would say the words he had so far not said. That he loved her. And perhaps she made some movement, some small sound, because he looked round, lowered the teddy, gave a sheepish smile.

'They wanted to talk.'

'Right.'

He grinned, rolled over, scooped the baby into his arms. 'Did you get through?'

'Mmm. Tomorrow morning, at nine-thirty.'

'*Tomorrow?*' he said in disappointment.

'Mmm. He can't fit me in today.'

'Then we will have to—improvise.'

'Mmm.' With a delightful blush staining her cheeks, she turned away. 'I'm going to have my shower.'

'And if his Lordship goes back to sleep I'll join you. If I may,' he tacked on softly.

Cheeks softly pink, she nodded, remembered other times when they'd shared the shower. And, when he did join her, as delightful as it was it wasn't *quite* the same. Not that she had any intention of saying so. Not by look, deed or words would she ever let him know that something was missing. That the memory of what he had done still lay between them. The fear that it might happen again.

And, during the rest of that day and night, when he finally shared her bed again, only she said the words she longed for him to say.

The next morning, walking back from the surgery, hands pushed into her coat pockets, she thought about it, wondered. What can't be cured must be endured— and that didn't help. But if this was all there would ever be it would be enough, she determined. She didn't think she could bear to lose him again, although he wasn't going to be *totally* pleased by the doctor's instructions. Any more than she was. She had the pills—but they wouldn't be effective for seven days. There was going to be a lot of improvisation, she thought with a rueful smile.

Hurrying into the house, stamping her boots to get rid of the snow, she smiled when he came to greet her, felt that overwhelming fullness, that hungry desire that she always felt each time she saw him.

He didn't smile back, and she slowly sobered. 'What is it?' she asked with a lick of fear. 'The baby?'

'No! No.' Helping her off with her coat and boots, he said quietly, 'We have a visitor.'

'Visitor?' she echoed stupidly.

'Yes. Nathalie.'

CHAPTER ELEVEN

'NATHALIE?' Gellis whispered in shock, and then her face firmed, determination tightening her mouth. 'I don't want her in my house, Sébastien.'

'I know, but I think you need to hear what she has to say.'

'Why?'

'Because you do.'

As she searched his face, the grimness in his eyes, a cold little feeling began inside, and she shivered. 'How long has she been here?'

'Five minutes. Come on into the lounge, get warm.'

She nodded, mind racing, then gripped his arm to stay him a moment. 'Are you…? Did she…?' Taking a deep breath, she blurted, 'You still find her—?'

'No,' he denied. He held her eyes, repeated softly, 'No.'

Then she could cope, she decided. If he no longer wanted Nathalie, she *could*. But a smile was too much to expect. Taking a deep breath, she squared her shoulders and walked ahead of him into the lounge.

Nathalie was standing facing the fire, elegant hands held out to the blaze. She looked svelte, blonde and hard.

'Nathalie?' Sébastien called softly, and she turned, gave Gellis a comprehensive glance, and smiled rather nastily.

'Have a nice little tête-à-tête in the hall, did you?' she asked sweetly.

Gellis gave a disgusted smile. 'You really think I would welcome into my home the woman responsible for the break-up of my marriage? Of robbing the baby of his father? Sébastien of his son?'

'Ah, yes,' she drawled. 'Sébastien has been telling me of his—son.'

'*Our* son,' Gellis corrected. 'So why are you here?'

'Because Sébastien and I are old—friends,' she explained, with a little smirk on her mouth that Gellis yearned to wipe off. 'I arrived soon after you left.'

'Five minutes before you returned,' Sébastien corrected, and Nathalie looked at him, gave another small smile.

'He was being very domestic,' she murmured silkily.

'Was he?'

'Yes.'

'He was also resistant to blackmail,' Sébastien put in coldly, and both women turned to look at him.

'Blackmail?' Gellis whispered.

'Yes.' Eyes on Nathalie, eyes that looked colder than a winter sea, he continued, 'She threatened to tell you the intimate details of our—relationship. I don't take kindly to threats. So tell her,' he invited.

Nathalie gave a slow smile that held not the slightest vestige of amusement. 'How very French. I hope your—wife, who is, of course, not French, is as understanding as you seem to think she is.'

'I'm not in the least understanding,' Gellis denied distastefully. 'But whilst we're on the subject of relationships perhaps you'd care to tell me about David.' And she had the satisfaction of seeing a flicker of uncertainty in the other woman's eyes.

'David?' she asked innocently.

'Yes, David. How did you know about him?'

She gave an elegant shrug.

'*How*, Nathalie?' Gellis persisted.

Examining her long, painted nails, mouth pursed, Nathalie said casually, 'Your mother told me.'

'My *mother*?' Gellis demanded in astonishment. 'You've never *met* my mother!'

'Ah, but I have. We met quite by accident last August. I saw her in the market in Lanion. Obviously English, she looked sufficiently like you for it to be a possibility.'

'But you didn't *know* me then...'

Nathalie gave another slow smile. 'Knew who you were. I'd been watching you for almost a week.'

'But you said you hadn't known he was married!'

'I lied,' she said without a shadow of shame.

'Yes,' Gellis agreed grimly. 'And when you came to the apartment pretending you didn't know which apartment was his...'

Nathalie shrugged.

'And so you got into conversation with my mother,' Gellis stated flatly. And knowing what a blabbermouth her mother could sometimes be...

'I can be quite charming when I choose,' Nathalie murmured. 'And your mother was so delighted by her son-in-law, her new grandson, assumed I knew more than I did about your lives together, was so pathetically grateful for your happiness after the disaster of David.'

'And what disaster would that be?'

'The break-up of your engagement, of course.'

Gellis gave a disgusted smile. 'He died, Nathalie.'

Shock briefly flickered in the other woman's eyes, and then she gave a wry smile. 'Any port in a storm.

Dead or alive, you could still have been in love with him.'

'But not having an *affair*!'

Nathalie's mouth twisted, and she laughed. 'You would have done the same.'

'No.'

'Then you're a fool,' she said derisively. 'I'm not. He was mine, and I wanted him back.'

'You said you already *had* him back,' Gellis said softly. 'Another lie, Nathalie?'

'*Non.* Just—hedging my bets; isn't that what you say? He'd already run out on me once, before he met you; I didn't intend for it to happen again.'

'And all's fair in love and war?'

'*Certainement.*'

'But you didn't tell him all this until *after* he came back. After he'd lost his memory. Why not tell him before?'

'I didn't need to. He was already intending to leave you.'

'But when he came back, not remembering either of us...'

'*Oui.* Interrogation over?' she asked sweetly. And when Gellis didn't say anything, just continued to watch her, she added harshly, 'He was mine. When he left, sold his restaurants, cut all ties with his old friends, it took me a long time to find him. He ran out on me—and *no* one does that. I wanted to know *why.*'

Yes, Gellis could understand that, and tried to imagine how she might have behaved had the roles been reversed. But she didn't think she would have lied. 'I wouldn't have lied,' she murmured.

'Wouldn't you?' Nathalie asked in disbelief. 'Then

you're more of a fool than I took you for. He married you on a whim, and was already regretting it. Sugar was never his style. Sébastien likes spice.'

'And so, just in case he was intending to come back to me, you used David to drive a wedge between us.'

'Because he didn't remember what had happened. Didn't remember that he'd been going to leave you for me. We were to meet up in Paris—only for some reason best known to himself he went to South America first.'

Glancing at Sébastien, at the sheer implacability of his face, Gellis did not know how she managed to speak, remain calm, when all she wanted to do was throw Nathalie out of the house and speak privately to Sébastien.

'And so you came to see me. I wonder you had the nerve.'

'Nerve? Oh, I have plenty of nerve. The French do. And, despite all he had done, I wanted him back. Was prepared to forgive him. And so I came to ask you where he was. Wanted to know if he'd asked you for a divorce.'

'I don't believe you.'

Nathalie shrugged with apparent indifference.

'If he'd wanted a divorce he would have asked me before he left. Not just sent a note.' Glancing again at Sébastien, at his closed face, Gellis almost despaired. But not in front of Nathalie. She would never give her the satisfaction. And if Nathalie could lie so blatantly about David, then she would probably lie about other things.

'If he was still in love with you,' Gellis said with dignity, 'then why did he marry me?'

Nathalie shrugged again. 'Rebound. Anger.' With

a mocking glance at Sébastien, she drawled, 'Always so stubborn. Once he made up his mind, he would never back down. But he grew tired of you, Gellis, finally admitted he'd made a mistake. That he should never have married you. That he still loved me. And then he had the accident, and remembered none of it,' she concluded.

'How did you know I was here?' Sébastien asked flatly.

Nathalie looked at him, gave a mocking smile. 'After you came to see me in Provence, I had you followed. It was really quite simple.'

'And didn't the fact that he came here tell you of his wishes, desires? That he wanted to be with me, not you?'

'*Non*. He might have come to ask for a divorce. Possibly did. Or was he summoned because you couldn't cope with his son?' she asked silkily. And, when Gellis refused to answer, she continued, 'And now he is being noble. The crying baby has turned into a child, and he feels—obliged to stay.'

'*Wishes* to stay,' he corrected.

She gave him a disgusted look. 'You do not like children. I imagine even *Gellis* knew that, but she was desperate, wasn't she? Needed something to hold the marriage together, and so she became pregnant.'

'Did she?' he asked coldly.

'Yes.' Turning back to Gellis, Nathalie gave a spiteful smile. 'But it won't work, Gellis. Or not for long. He'll soon get bored with playing house.'

'As he did with you?'

'*Non,*' she denied. 'Because we weren't *playing*. Did you never wonder why he didn't tell you about me? About his past life? I knew the *real* Sébastien. You only got the shadow.'

'Did I?'

'Yes.'

'Then if that is all you have to say,' Gellis replied with quiet dignity, 'I would like you to leave. Now.'

'How pathetic you are. To want a man who doesn't want you.'

'The same could be said of you. It all depends on your perspective, doesn't it?'

With another dismissive shrug, Nathalie turned aside to pick up her coat and bag from the chair. Facing Sébastien, she gave him a long, mocking look. 'When you get bored with nappy-changing, call me. I might even take you back.'

'Kind of you.'

She gave a mirthless smile, a deliberately provocative pat on his cheek.

He neither moved nor spoke. Just watched her, his face cold.

No one helped her on with her coat, no one saw her out. But as she reached the front door Sébastien called her.

'Nathalie?'

And when she halted, turned, he said flatly, insistently, 'Don't come back, will you?'

The front door was slammed in answer.

'How will she get home?' Gellis asked without interest.

'She has a taxi waiting along the road.'

With a little shrug of her own, she continued to stare blindly before her. She hadn't wanted to know the details, but then, her mind could so easily supply its own. Images of Sébastien and Nathalie locked in

an intimate embrace. Of Nathalie and Sébastien naked, making love on a wide bed. 'No,' she whispered.
'No.' Clutching the mantelshelf for support, she
bowed her head onto her hands, closed her eyes in
defeat.

'Do you still have the note?' he asked quietly.

'What?'

'The note, and a pen and paper.'

'With a shuddery sigh, not understanding, she went
to get them, handed them to him.

Perching on the arm of the chair, he read the note,
then folded it and began to write. When he'd finished,
he handed both pieces of paper to her. 'Does it look
like the same handwriting?'

Staring blindly from one to the other, she gave a
helpless shrug. 'Not exactly. But then your writing
before the accident might be different to now.' Glancing at him, she asked hesitantly, 'You don't think you
sent it?'

Still frowning, still thoughtful, he slowly shook his
head. '*Non.* I think Nathalie did. Whatever I was,
whatever I had been, I can't believe I would be so
cruel as to send you a terse note saying I would not
be back. Neither do I think she and I were lovers—
not whilst *we* were married, anyway.'

But maybe they had been.

'And I don't like her. Am not attracted to her. I am
to you, and, presumably, tastes don't change… Supposing,' he began carefully, 'that I hadn't left you? If
it hadn't been for the note, and Nathalie turning up,
what would you have believed?'

'That you'd had an accident,' she murmured
painfully.

'And so you would have searched more diligently—'

'I *did* search!' she cried.

'But not as hard as if you thought I'd had an accident,' he persisted.

'And so it's *my* fault?' she swung round to demand.

'No! No, I'm only saying—'

'The police wouldn't *look*! They were sympathetic, but it happened all the time. You'd sent a *note*!'

'But why in God's name would I go to *South America*?'

'I don't know!' she cried tearfully. 'I no longer know *what* to think.' Eyes anguished, she added, 'And I can't bear for it to be spoiled. Not again. Oh, Sébastien, not again!'

'No,' he agreed thickly. Stepping towards her, he pulled her into his arms, held her tight, his own eyes closed with the same defeat. 'I can't imagine cheating on you,' he murmured against her hair. 'For why? I can't prove it, can't deny it with any certainty, but it doesn't *feel* right.' Rubbing one hand slowly up and down her back, hoping to comfort, soothe, he asked bleakly, 'Can you live with that, Gellis? Not knowing?'

With a painful sigh, that feeling of helplessness back with a vengeance, she leaned away so that she could see into his face. 'How long were you intending to stay here, Sébastien?'

'For as long as you would have me,' he said simply.

'For Christmas?'

'Yes. And Easter, and summer. I would have to go back to France from time to time, but...' Taking a deep breath, he continued, 'I can't tell you that I loved you, because I only know that I love you *now*. I want you, need you, need to see the baby—but to say that I loved you might be a lie. And I don't want to lie to you. I want to *make* love to you. I want to be able to touch you, kiss you, but…' Briefly closing his eyes again, he said heavily, 'Without memory, without *knowing*…'

'Because supposing Nathalie was right? Suppose you do get your memory back and find out that she was telling the truth?'

'Yes,' he admitted honestly. 'And yet I can't *imagine* that it's the truth. Can't imagine that I won't feel as I feel now.' Easing her away, he held her shoulders, stared down into her distressed face. 'I need to take charge of my life, Gellis. Need to know the truth. And if I can't know the truth, then I have to put it behind me and begin again. I won't—can't—live my life like this.'

'No,' she agreed quietly. 'What did she want? For you to go back with her?'

'Yes,' he admitted simply. 'When I refused, she became angry.'

'She didn't look angry.'

'No.'

'But she won't give up, will she? If she can't have you herself, she will do her best to split *us* up. When we first met,' she continued slowly, 'when we first made love, I asked you why you had been reluctant to kiss me, and you said that I looked like a lady easy to hurt.'

'Did I?'

'Yes,' she whispered. 'And you said that you didn't want to do that.'

'And you think I said it because of Nathalie?'

'I don't know.'

'She can only hurt us if we let her,' he said quietly.

'Yes.'

'Which is why I wanted her to tell you all that she'd said to me before you came home. I told her I was staying, and she laughed, said that after what she had to say to you you wouldn't *want* me to stay. It was a chance I had to take, Gellis.'

'Yes,' she agreed emptily, but she hadn't wanted to know the details; just the thought of it made her feel sick. 'But our marriage wasn't in trouble—I would have *known*. And I didn't deliberately get pregnant to hold you. That was her lie, not mine.'

'Yes.'

'But you can't *know* that, can you?'

'Gellis,' he said quietly as he gently framed her anguished face, 'if you tell me it's true, then I believe you. Did you see the doctor?'

'Hmm? Oh, yes.' With a smile that was painful to behold, she added, 'We have to wait seven days before they're effective.'

'Oh. And will we need them, Gellis? The pills?'

Eyes flooding with tears, she buried her face against his sweater. Voice muffled, she said, 'I love you. And until we know the truth, if we ever do... Oh, Sébastien, I couldn't bear to go back to living a half-life, but if you...'

'No! No.' Arms tightening round her, he rocked her back and forth, rubbed his face against her hair. 'It was a lie, Gellis. It *has* to have been a lie. We both have to hold onto that. Nathalie lied.'

'Yes,' she agreed, but knew that it would always be between them. Taking a determined breath, she straightened, smiled. 'Was the baby good?'

'Yes. Not a peep out of him.'

'And you're not staying just because...?'

'No. And I like being domestic,' he added with a funny little smile. A smile that brought fresh tears to her eyes.

'It hurts, Sébastien.'

'I know. And if I could have saved you the pain of it I would have. But if I'd got rid of her before you came home she would have found another way of telling you. An even more painful way, perhaps. Nathalie is not someone who can be threatened—and I won't be blackmailed. But what was I *like*, Gellis? Dear God, what sort of a man *was* I?'

'A good man,' she stated quietly and with conviction. But had he been? And he'd taken a chance, hadn't he? Did he know how much she loved him? Know that she would put up with almost anything to keep him? And now she would always wonder, wouldn't she? Wonder whether one day he would grow bored and want to leave. 'Was she really only here five minutes?'

'Yes. You once said that I must believe what I chose to believe—and so, now, I have to say those words back to you. Despite what she said, implied, she was only here five minutes. I stood in the window watching for you, as I always watch for you when you're out. She tried to kiss me; perhaps she thought that if I was covered in lipstick you would be...'

'Angry? Hurt? Jealous? As I am,' she said painfully.

'I don't *want* her, Gellis. And I won't let this memory loss ruin my life, won't—can't—*afford* to let it dictate my actions. The rest of my life has to start

somewhere, and I want it to be here, with you and
Sébastien.

'Even if I was like Nathalie said I was—which isn't
a comforting thought—I'm not like that *now*, and if I
do get my memory back, then at least I will remember
how she has been, what she has done—and I can't
believe I would be so lacking in judgement that I
would ever want her back. So lacking in *sense*!'

'But if you did love her,' Gellis said sadly, 'sense
wouldn't come into it.' Didn't she know that better
than anyone? Forcing another smile, she stated firmly,
'The rest of our lives starts now. December the—
eighteenth!' she exclaimed in surprise. 'And this time
next week will be Christmas Day.'

'And the pills will be effective,' he murmured with
a quirky smile. But, like hers, his smile was a little
bit forced. Strained.

'Yes. Seven days of innovation before… I'd better
go and see if the baby's awake. It's nearly time for
his lunch.'

Sébastien nodded, slowly released her, and so she
didn't see the bleakness in his eyes as she walked
through the door. Any more than he saw hers.

For six days they pretended—smiled whenever either
caught the other looking—and their lovemaking was
gentle, restrained, because Nathalie was there between
them and neither could forget.

The tree was a poignant reminder of another year.
For Gellis, anyway. The gifts were a desperate promise that lacked hope. And would the day come, she
wondered as she gazed blindly at the beautifully decorated pine, when one or the other would admit that it
wasn't enough? That Nathalie's words had poisoned

the promise? How often did he wonder if the words were true? Did he imagine making love to the other woman? Try to understand how it might have been? If it was more exciting than making love to Gellis? As often as *she* wondered?

'Gellis?'

'In here,' she murmured, then turned to smile at him.

'You've got a flat rear tyre,' he informed her.

'Have I?' she asked vaguely, not even remotely interested. 'I wonder how that happened?'

Exasperated, he said shortly, 'Gellis, you must have noticed when you drove home from the village yesterday that something was wrong!'

She shook her head, then looked thoughtful. 'We-ell, I just assumed that snow had built up on the tyres. Or something.'

'Don't you *check* the tyres before you get in the car?'

'No. Do you?'

He gave her a look of disgust.

'That means you don't,' she murmured, and gave a sly smile.

Refusing to answer on the grounds that men don't have to, he said piously, 'I'll go and change it for you.'

'Thank you.'

'And then I'll go and pick up the turkey.'

'Thank you. Don't forget the vegetables.'

'I won't.' As he turned away, she just caught the edge of a twitched lip. But when he had gone out to the garage the gloom settled back. Tomorrow they would be able to make love. Did he still want to? And next Christmas? Where would they be then? Still here? Back in France? She'd asked if he wanted to go back, and he'd said no. Not yet. Because there was still an air of impermanence about their relationship?

Little Sébastien would probably be walking into everything; the number of presents would be greater. A train set, trucks… Hard to imagine him toddling round, laughing, excited. But would his father be here?

Staring at the gifts, at the presents she had bought Sébastien—an expensive fountain pen, a sweater—she wished she had bought something else, something better, more imaginative. But she hadn't been able to think of anything. Last year, there had been silly presents to make him laugh. This year, there was a boring pen and a sweater.

She'd bought presents for the baby. Clothing mostly, some fluffy toys, building bricks; he would be sitting up soon. She had thought, before Nathalie had come, that she couldn't ask for anything more, just to be friends and lovers with Sébastien, parents. But she did need more. Needed to know she was loved. Needed to know he hadn't cheated. With a deep sigh, she went to make some coffee.

Staring out at the snowy garden, at the birds scrabbling for the food she'd put out, she heard Sébastien grunt, then curse, then a yell and the clank of something metallic hitting the concrete of the garage floor. Whoops. With a little grimace, she wondered whose fault that was going to be. Hers, probably.

Expecting the back door to be wrenched open, expecting complaint, she waited, then frowned when there was nothing. No sound, no voice, no nothing. Tilting her head the better to listen, she heard a low groan, a faint thud. Puzzled, she opened the back

door, peered into the garage, called hesitantly,
'Sébastien?'

Nothing.

Her frown deeper, she stepped out, walked round
the end of the jacked-up car—and saw Sébastien
hunched on the floor, his back against the wall. His
left wrist was clasped in his right hand, and his head
was bowed over his knees. He was shaking, dragging
deep, noisy breaths into his lungs and shaking.

Alarmed, she hurried over, crouched beside him,
and, one hand on his back, whispered worriedly,
'Sébastien?'

He groaned again, gripped his wrist tighter, and in
the dim light she saw blood slowly dripping from his
left hand. 'Oh, what have you *done*?' Men were such
babies. 'Let me have a look.' As she reached out to
take his hand, he gave a violent jump that startled her
so much, she sat down with a thump.

'Sébastien…' she began in exasperation, and then
stopped. Stared at his face as he slowly raised his
head. He looked grey. 'What?' she whispered in a
frightened little voice.

'It hurts,' he gasped. 'Like rushing through a tunnel
with no brakes. Flickers, lights—too fast to grasp.'
Shutting his eyes, teeth gritted, he leaned his head
back against the wall. 'Tumbling, buffeted from all
sides.' A deep frown etching his forehead, he rolled
his head towards her, opened his eyes—but quite
clearly didn't see her, only what was in his head.

'I had a flat tyre, and I had to get to the airport,
get home… There was a truck, and the driver said he
could take me… I asked the hotel to let the hire company know, tell them to collect the car, and I tossed

my bag and jacket in the truck…' Eyes closed tight, he strained to find more, and couldn't.

Hands shaking as much as his, she gripped his arm, stared worriedly at his ashen face. 'Where are you? *Where?* South America?'

'Yes, the middle of nowhere. A young boy found me, went to fetch the local authorities. I was lying on a dusty track. There had obviously been an accident of some sort—there was broken glass from a head-light, scrapes against some rocks—but there was no sign of the truck or driver, no sign of any belongings, papers I might have had—and I didn't know how I *got* there—or who I was,' he whispered.

'Go on.'

Frowning with the memory, hands clenched tight, he continued, 'A local doctor stitched me up, and I was housed in the local jail. They made what en-quiries they could, but we weren't near a big town, weren't near *anything*, and I was impatient, aggres-sive; my head hurt like hell, and it was all taking too long! They had no fax, the telephone only seemed to work when it felt like it—and I was a problem they didn't need. I felt ill, was probably concussed, I didn't speak the language.

'Oh, God, Gellis. Dirty and unshaven, I began to think I would never get out of there, never find out who I was, that I would stay there as a curiosity, a nuisance, until I died of old age!' Rubbing the heels of his hands against his aching forehead, liberally transferring the blood from his palm, he continued slowly, 'We were near the coast, and I used to walk down, stare at the sea—and that's where I met Jan Vermeer. A Dutchman. He ran some sort of cargo service in an old tramp steamer…' With a brief laugh, he added, 'God knows how he made a living.

'Anyway, he asked me if I needed a berth. And I said yes. Anything was better than—waiting. He said he could get me some papers, to pay him back when I could… Probably stupid, but I just wanted to be *doing* something!'

Afraid to hope, frightened of what he might say about Nathalie, Gellis pleaded, 'But what were you *doing* there?'

'Doing?' he asked vaguely. With another deep shudder, he continued disjointedly, 'I told you—I had a flat tyre. I tried to change it, but the wheel nuts were on too tight; I couldn't get them undone. And in a temper, frustration, I wrenched at them and the wheel brace slipped—as it did just now—and I hurt my hand.'

Lowering his left hand, he stared blindly at the long gash in his palm, at the blood dripping slowly to the garage floor. 'And it all came back,' he whispered. 'I felt faint, dizzy, sat back here—and it's like everything crashing in at once.' With a shiver, a snatched, quivering breath, he slowly focused on her frightened face. 'Dear God, Gellis, it's coming back.'

'Should I get a doctor?' she asked worriedly.

'Doctor?' he frowned. 'No.'

Eyes fixed on his face, almost afraid to look away, she settled herself beside him. Unmindful of the cold garage floor, unmindful of the chill, she put her arms round him, held him tight. 'Go on,' she urged. 'What happened before?'

Still frowning, still searching for the elusive memories, he murmured, 'I threw the wheel brace in the road, and that's when the truck driver…'

'No. Before. What were you *doing* there?'

'Sorry, it's all muddled together. I had a phone call from Claude.'

'Claude?'

'Yes. He and François were old friends from when I was a child. We played together, did everything together, and I hadn't seen them for years. He said François was in South America in some dreadful hospital, and without money he couldn't get treatment. He'd been trying to persuade the embassy to do something…'

'And because François was a friend, and because you do things on impulse,' Gellis said gently, 'you went to help.'

'Yes.'

'But why didn't you *tell* me?'

'Because I didn't want to worry you. I could be there and back in a few days, so I told you I was going to meet someone in Paris… Didn't you ever wonder why I had taken my passport with me?'

'No,' she replied helplessly. Or not until after she'd got the note, and then she'd *known* why. Or thought she had.

'And so I caught the train to Paris, flew out… But when I got there he was dead,' he explained sadly. 'And so all I wanted was to come home.'

'I'm so sorry.'

'Yes. He'd been backpacking, got some sort of virus, infection—I don't know. I didn't understand all that the hospital told me…'

'And you weren't going to divorce me?'

'What? No. No!' he denied violently. Hooking her against him, he held her tight in his arms. 'I couldn't find out who I was, Gellis,' he said sadly. 'Everywhere I went, trying, trying... And then I found you in Portsmouth...'

'You *were* coming back?' she asked hesitantly.

'What?'

'You were coming back to me? From South America?'

'Yes! Oh, Gellis, yes.' Closing his eyes, he inhaled the scent of her, the warmth—and he didn't think he could bear it. Four months of not seeing her, and then treating her like an interloper, a nobody. And as his mind filled with all those images, the way he'd been in Portsmouth, he groaned. It hurt. Dear God, how it hurt—but he didn't say the words she needed to hear. Didn't know that he hadn't. Didn't see the way she watched him, her heart in her eyes.

'And Nathalie?'

Opening his eyes, he stared at her. 'Nathalie?' And memory rushed back. His face grim, he said flatly, 'Ah, yes. Nathalie.'

'You were lovers?'

'No,' he denied. 'I knew her in Provence. We went out a couple of times—dinner, the theatre, drinks— but that was all. I was wealthy, Gellis, and she was— an opportunist. Her father owned a restaurant—and thought it would be nice to own a chain. By marrying into them,' he added cynically.

'And she couldn't accept that I didn't return her feelings—*wouldn't* accept it. She'd allowed people to think we were in love, hinted at an engagement, and, when I made it plain that there would be no engagement, no joining of restaurants, she was angry. Spiteful. She said I would be sorry—as I was,' he added in a voice as hard and harsh as the one he'd used in Portsmouth. And there was an expression of such *an-*

ger on his strong face that she squeezed his arm, tried to divert him.

Looking at her, he said emphatically, 'We were not lovers, Gellis. I didn't cheat. And I did not send her a note. I told her to her face.'

Thank God. Oh, thank God. Letting out a long breath, a breath she hadn't been aware she'd been holding, Gellis asked, 'And in Brittany? Did you see her there?'

'No,' he denied with a frown. 'My God, do you think I would have gone off to South America and left you if I'd known she was there?'

'So it was all lies?'

'Yes.'

'But she must have been there, watching us. Jealous of our happiness, do you think?'

'Determined on revenge,' he amended flatly. 'I would guess she felt humiliated. She'd told people we would be married, and when I walked away, left, she determined to make me pay. As she did. Do you have any idea what these last few weeks have done to me, Gellis? Thinking I was a cheat, a liar... I could kill her. And I want to make *her* pay now.'

'No,' Gellis said softly.

'No? She destroyed your trust, your love...'

'No, not my love.'

'Oh, Gellis,' he sighed.

'Yeah,' she agreed. Suddenly aware how chilled she was, how chilled he must be, she stirred, turned her head to ease the stiffness. 'Let's go inside,' she urged gently. 'You can tell me the rest later. We need to clean that hand up.'

Uncomprehending for a moment, Sébastien stared at his hand, almost surprised to see the gash, the blood. And then he nodded. Like a sleepwalker, he got to his feet, helped her up and they went inside.

When she'd cleaned his hand and bandaged it, washed the smeared blood from his forehead, she led him into the lounge, made up the fire and went to pour the coffee. Deliberately keeping her mind blank, empty of hope, need, she carried the coffee in, put his beside him and knelt by his feet. Eyes fixed on his face as he stared unseeingly into the flames, she couldn't even begin to comprehend how he was feeling.

'I'm two different people, Gellis. Three,' he corrected, frowning. 'I remember how I was before we met—arrogant, impatient, and, yes, sometimes ruthless. Even without Nathalie, it was a life I came to hate. The shallowness, the greed. And then I moved to Collioure, and I was—different. The people were different.'

Glancing at her, face still sombre, he continued quietly, 'And now I keep thinking about that day you left me at the château. Keep seeing your face, your anguish and despair... I could have lost you,' he murmured. 'Four months of—' Eyes focusing so suddenly it made her blink, he sat up straighter, stared at her. 'And I had a child!'

'Yes,' she agreed worriedly.

'Oh, dear God.' Burying his head in his hands, he stayed like that for some moments, then slowly raised his head. 'Where is he?'

'In his carry-cot,' she answered gently as she pointed across the room. 'He's asleep.'

He relaxed fractionally, nodded. 'I was suddenly afraid he wasn't real.' With an unsteady breath, he got to his feet and walked over to stare down at his son, then touch his finger gently to one soft cheek. 'I should never have gone. Never have left you. Should have been there. I've missed four months of his life. Missed him focusing. Missed him chortling,' he said sadly. 'I should have looked after you—I missed it all, Gellis.'

'Yes,' she agreed compassionately.

'Days, moments that can never be recaptured, all gone.' Moving his finger to the baby's fist, he gave a faint smile when Sébastien grasped it in his sleep, held it tight. 'I love him,' he said thickly.

Her voice equally thick, she nodded. 'I know.'

Raising his eyes to hers, eyes that looked too bright, too green, he asked, 'Did you know why I never wanted children?'

'You said because you wanted me to yourself.'

'Yes, but that wasn't entirely true. I was afraid I would be jealous, leave them feeling shut out and lonely. My parents did that.'

'Oh, Sébastien.'

'I was afraid,' he confessed, 'that I would not be able to share you.'

With a heavy sigh, he walked back to the sofa, collapsed as though boneless and stared at his coffee as though surprised to find it there. Picking it up in a hand that still shook, he took a sip, and then he leaned back, rested his head against the cushions.

Wanting to comfort him, but almost afraid to, wanting to smooth back his hair, reassure him, Gellis took a deep breath and murmured quietly, 'There are a lot of people like Nathalie. You read about them in the papers, about their—fixations. They need help.'

'So did I,' he said grimly, then winced.

'Headache?'

'Yes; it's not important. I owned a chain of restaurants—I told you that, didn't I?'

'Yes.'

'Nathalie and her father wanted into them. Wanted to become partners. She thought we would make a good partnership—as husband and wife. But I didn't want a wife. And women like Nathalie think they only have to demand it for it to happen. She refused to believe that I didn't find her attractive. And her father refused to believe that I hadn't seduced her.'

'And so you sold up and left.'

'Yes. Sold everything. Packed everything I needed into two suitcases and caught the train to—wherever.'

'Without telling them?'

'Without telling them I'd sold the restaurants,' he qualified. 'I'd had enough, Gellis. Not only of Nathalie—I was tired of the life, of the sameness, the same boring people, the same boring conversations; it had all begun to seem so pointless. I lived the life my parents had lived without ever wanting to, intending to.

'When I graduated in law,' he murmured with a funny smile, 'I travelled, roamed the world—made money,' he added cynically. 'I have interests in boatyards in America, Spain. And then, when my parents died in a yachting accident—together, as they had always been—I came back to France. A friend of my father had a restaurant he wanted to sell, so I bought it, then another and another, discovered I liked to cook...'

'And then got bored?'

'Not with cooking, with the life. And so I came to Collioure. The people weren't grasping, or pompous, or jealous. Everyone helped each other out. Struggling artists, struggling businesses... There was a *kindness* there that I hadn't experienced before. And I felt—at home. And then I met you.'

Turning his head on the cushion, he stared at her exquisite face. 'You were everything I'd never known. Warm, funny, gentle. You *cared* about people, Gellis. You didn't care about money or status. You have a generous spirit. When Marie had no one to help in the shop when her mother was taken ill, you didn't even think about it—just pitched in to help. You didn't even speak the language very well. The people I had known would never have done that.

'But because of the life I'd led I didn't know if one day I would get bored, restless, and so I didn't want to hurt you by entering into a commitment that I might not be able to keep. But the longer I knew you, the harder it became to deny. I tried to imagine a life without you, and couldn't. Nathalie and I were never lovers, Gellis. Not before our marriage, nor during. I give you my word. You believe me?'

'Yes,' she whispered.

'And I can't—won't—ever forgive her for what she tried to do,' he said grimly. 'For hurting you. Doing it to me is one thing. Doing it to you is entirely another.'

'Yes. So she did send the note?'

'Yes; there was no one else who *could* have done so.'

'But what did she think she would *gain*?' Gellis asked, puzzled. 'She had no knowledge that you wouldn't come back. No knowledge that you'd gone to South America! And if you *had* come back...'

'She'd sown a seed,' he said grimly. 'Caused trouble.'

'Vengeful,' she murmured.

'Yes. She'd convinced herself that I'd betrayed her, and so set out to punish me. And succeeded,' he added quietly. Turning to face her, eyes anxious, he asked, 'It's not too late?'

'Too late?'

'For us. I love you,' he said simply. 'I love you so much it's a physical ache. I look at you now, now that I remember you, and I cannot conceive how I could ever have forgotten. The way you touch things, the way you move, your smile, your elegance, your— gentleness...'

Swallowing hard, she perched on the arm of the sofa, put her arms round him and leaned her head against his. 'I love you too.' But it hadn't all been said. Resolved. 'You remember it all?' Gellis asked quietly. 'Remember asking me to marry you? How we felt about each other?'

'Yes. I remember it all. And it hurts. That for four months of my life I was—lost. That you had to cope alone. That all I did was cause you pain.'

Touching gentle fingers to his face, a distant sadness in her eyes, she said softly, 'I loved you, Sébastien. So very much.'

'Loved?' he asked as he turned to look up at her. 'Past tense?'

'No. Past and present. Just to see you, feel you near, walk into a room where you are, it's like—falling in love all over again. Each and every time. But there wasn't fear then—there is now. Now, because of the accident, I'm aware of mortality.'

'Not because of David?' he asked curiously. 'You lost one love; weren't you afraid of losing another?'

'No,' she denied on a spurt of surprise. 'I wasn't.

It was as though our lives were charmed. Meant to be. Sounds silly, but that's how I felt.'

'But not now?'

'No,' she denied sombrely. 'Now, each moment is precious, to be savoured. You leave me defenceless, Sébastien. Without you, I'm lost. It's frightening. And this past week,' she continued quietly, 'those few days in France... Wanting you, almost hating you, has been so very hard, and I have been so tired, and so very afraid. What we had was special, the greatest love story ever told, and it seemed so unfair that it should end because you did not remember how we had loved. The last four months have changed us both—but I don't love you less, just ache for you, for your pain. Yearn to have it as it was. But we have the rest of our lives, don't we?'

'Yes. And I need to hold you,' he said thickly. Scooping her off the arm of the sofa, he pulled her onto his lap, held her impossibly tight. Her head on his shoulder, his face against hers, he stared at the room—at the tree, the baby's cot, the fire. So nearly lost. Carols had been softly playing on the radio, barely heard by either of them; it was only when they stopped that they really registered. 'A quiet Christmas this year,' Sébastien murmured. 'Just the three of us.'

'Yes. Just the three of us.' Raising her head, Gellis stared at him, at his dear face, stared into green-flecked eyes that held so much love, so much sadness, and smiled, a smile that was shaken, wobbly. 'I love you,' she whispered huskily.

'And I you.'

'And tomorrow—' She broke off, her eyes widening in shock. 'We didn't get the turkey!'

'What?'

'We didn't get the *turkey*!' she repeated urgently.

Staring at her, he suddenly switched his attention to the clock. 'What time do the shops shut?'

'Don't know.' Hurrying out to the hall, she grabbed her boots, began to drag them on.

'What are you doing?' he demanded from behind her. 'I'll go.'

'No, you won't; you're to stay here and rest. I'll go.' Grabbing her coat, she pressed a quick, hard kiss on his mouth and ran. Shrugging into her coat as she went, laughing, she hurried down to the village and arrived, gasping, in the butcher's just as he was about to close. She grinned at him triumphantly. 'Forgot!' she exclaimed breathlessly.

'So I gathered. I was just going to bring it round. In fact, I *will* bring it round.' He smiled. 'It's *heavy*, Gellis—and do your coat up.'

'Yes, sir, thank you.' With a gesture that surprised both of them, she reached across to kiss his cheek. 'Happy Christmas.'

Feeling somewhat dazzled, he returned automatically, 'Happy Christmas.' And then he smiled. Extraordinarily pleased to see her looking so happy, vibrant, he had the foolish wish that he were a great deal younger—and slimmer. With a rueful shake of his head, he watched her dash along to the grocer's, watched that glorious plait swing widely and wondered just what had made her forget her shopping. Having met the Frenchman, he could make a very good guess.

Closing and locking his door, he crunched along to his van, carrying Gellis's turkey. And the goodwill that had been rather sadly lacking over the last few washed days returned. Happiness was somehow con-

tagious. And then he spontaneously decided to tak
the goodwill just a little bit further.

Jumping into the van, he turned it, drove along t
the grocer's and stopped.

Laughing, cheeks glowing, Gellis returned to th
house twenty minutes after she'd left. As the va
stopped, the front door was opened and she sa
Sébastien outlined in amber light. Waiting for he
Feeling warmed and loved and special, she climbe
out, as did the butcher with her shopping. Sébastie
met them at the gate.

'Thank you,' he said warmly. *'Joyeux Noël.'*

'And to you.' With another smile for Gellis, th
butcher went home to his wife—who rather wondere
at the change from lugubrious to laughing in just th
space of a few hours. Not that she was complaining

'I think he thought me mad,' Gellis laughed as sh
closed the front door behind them.

'Non, I think he thought you beautiful,' Sébastie
corrected as he dumped the shopping by the coat rac

'Nonsense. What?' she asked happily.

'Come here,' he ordered softly.

And that lovely spiral began inside, that beautif
excitement born of desire, of anticipation. Shruggin
out of her coat as she moved towards him, sh
dropped it on the floor. Walking into his waiting arm
she stared into his beloved face. 'What?' she repeate
softly.

'This,' he murmured huskily as he touched his li
to the corner of hers, began to work his way alor
her delightful mouth. 'Four months since I have bee
able to do this. Four months of not knowing I wante
to.' Scooping her up, he carried her into the loung

placed her gently on the sofa and bent to tug off her
boots.

'But you know it now, don't you?'

'Yes,' he agreed thickly as he knelt before her. 'I
now it now.' Like a blind man reaching out, he
touched his fingers to her face, stared deep into her
lovely eyes. 'I've been sitting here, waiting, thinking.
So *much* to think about, so much to put in place.

'My head still feels scrambled, unsure, afraid to
think too deeply—afraid it will all go away again. It
feels like the whole world is crammed into my chest,
my heart. And I keep remembering how I asked how
it was, to show me, make me remember something of
how it had been. How could I have forgotten, Gellis?
Something that special should never be forgotten.'

'I don't know,' she soothed gently as she held her
palm against his cheek. 'But it's over now.' Moving
her eyes to his mouth, she urged softly, thickly, 'Kiss
me. The way you used to.' And just the thought of it
unfurled that deep pain in her stomach, that ache in
her heart, made her breathing faster, her pulses race.

His hazel eyes darkened, that passionate mouth
parted as they just stared at each other, drank in each
other's features.

'When you got out of the van just now, happy,
laughing, it was as though something inside me broke.
I love you so much. You're my whole world, Gellis.
Smile for me now,' he demanded raggedly as he
moved to sit beside her, draw her slowly into his
arms. 'It's been such a long time in the wilderness.'

'I can't.' Closing her eyes, she touched her mouth
to his, felt that familiar kick against her ribs as he
gently touched his tongue against hers. 'Kiss me

slowly,' she murmured. 'Make love to me in French
You always made love to me in French.'

'Because it's a language made for love.'

'Yes. Let's go home.'

'To France?'

'Yes. I miss my friends.'

'Don't you want to stay in England now that you've
had a taste of it again?'

'No. I love England, but France is now my home.'

'*Bien*. We will go home after Christmas. I'll contact
Gérard, get him to find us a bigger apartment, or a
house—with a nursery. And now there has been far
too much talking.'

Lifting his legs, he leaned sideways, pulled her to
lie beside him, beneath him, and bent to kiss her
Slowly. Deep, drugging kisses that began at the corner
of her mouth, kisses that became more urgent, more
demanding, kisses that sent heartbeats racing. Kisses
that made the head too heavy, the neck too weak
Kisses that blurred the mind, the senses—and yet
alerted every nerve-end, sensitised the flesh, until
kisses were no longer enough.

'How many more days?' he asked thickly.

'One,' she answered.

'Take a chance?'

'Oh, yes.'

Staring up at him, eyes blurred with desire, revel
ling in the warmth of him, the weight of him, she
moved her finger to the small scar on his cheekbone
'How did you do this?'

Settling his weight more comfortably, enjoying his
own arousal against her exquisite shape, enjoying jus
staring at her, feeling her against him, he murmured

azily, 'I went sailing because you said I used to. The
oom caught me, knocked me overboard.'

'Why weren't you wearing a safety line?'

'Don't remember.'

'Liar.'

And he smiled. A slow, extraordinarily beautiful,
xtraordinarily loving smile. And then he kissed her
gain, because he needed her kisses so very much.
Kissed her with slow enjoyment, kissed her with the
memory of other kisses, and felt his heartbeat
uicken, his pulses race.

'I wonder how impossible it would be to remove
ll our clothes without actually untangling ourselves?'
e said throatily. *'C'est possible?'*

Her smile equally slow, drowsy, her accent as
rench as his, she agreed, 'Eminently possible.'

'But I'm injured,' he murmured softly. 'So you
ave to do it.'

Feeling boneless, warmly excited, she began with
is sweater.

'Music to love by,' he whispered as the carol ser-
ice resumed, and they were half-naked.

'Yes. Hips up.'

He lifted his hips.

'A fire to keep us warm.'

Moving her face against his naked chest like a kit-
n, rubbing her bare toes against his calf, she stared
the flames. 'Do you remember the first time we
ade love?' she asked softly.

'Yes.'

And she smiled, raised her head.

'I undid your plait. Like this.' Tugging the band
ee, he began to untangle the long strands, gave a
gh of pleasure as the hair flowed round her shoul-

ders. As he arranged it across her full breasts, his ha
zel eyes darkened. 'Make love to me,' he urged, hi
voice thick, uneven, more accented than usual. 'Th
way you used to.'

Her smile dying, dark eyes sleepy with desire, sh
touched her mouth to his, closed her eyes the bette
to revel in the feel of his naked body against hers, le
out her breath on a sigh of exquisite, tearful pleasure
'Welcome home,' she breathed softly. 'Oh, Sébastien
welcome home.'

The lights on the Christmas tree winking brightly
curtains drawn against the dark, the baby sleeping i
his cot, and with the small sounds the fire made, th
two figures entwined on the sofa made their ow
Christmas wishes come true.

LYNN ERICKSON

Night Whispers

Someone is watching her every move...

Anna Dunning is living a nightmare. A stalker
is on the prowl and her only hope is a tough
ex-cop—but can she trust him?

*"...shadowy and suspenseful, leaving the reader with
a creepy, unsettled feeling of
expectation."*—**Publishers Weekly**

1-55166-178-0
AVAILABLE FROM DECEMBER 1997

MIRA®

WINTER WARMERS

How would you like to win a year's supply of Mills & Boon® books? Well you can and they're FREE! Simply complete the competition below and send it to us by 30th June 1998. The first five correct entries picked after the closing date will each win a year's subscription to the Mills & Boon series of their choice. What could be easier?

THERMAL SOCKS   RAINCOAT   RADIATOR

TIGHTS   WOOLY HAT   CARDIGAN

BLANKET   SCARF   LOG FIRE

WELLINGTONS   GLOVES   JUMPER

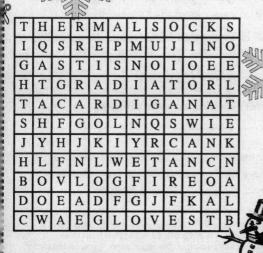

T	H	E	R	M	A	L	S	O	C	K	S
I	Q	S	R	E	P	M	U	J	I	N	O
G	A	S	T	I	S	N	O	I	O	E	E
H	T	G	R	A	D	I	A	T	O	R	L
T	A	C	A	R	D	I	G	A	N	A	T
S	H	F	G	O	L	N	Q	S	W	I	E
J	Y	H	J	K	I	Y	R	C	A	N	K
H	L	F	N	L	W	E	T	A	N	C	N
B	O	V	L	O	G	F	I	R	E	O	A
D	O	E	A	D	F	G	J	F	K	A	L
C	W	A	E	G	L	O	V	E	S	T	B

C7L

Please turn over for details of how to enter ➪

HOW TO ENTER

There is a list of twelve items overleaf all of which are used to keep you warm and dry when it's cold and wet. Each of these items, is hidden somewhere in the grid for you to find. They may appear forwards, backwards or diagonally. As you find each one, draw a line through it. When you have found all twelve, don't forget to fill in the coupon below, pop this page into an envelope and post it today—you don't even need a stamp! Hurry competition ends 30th June 1998.

Mills & Boon Winter Warmers Competition
FREEPOST CN81, Croydon, Surrey, CR9 3WZ

EIRE readers send competition to PO Box 4546, Dublin 24.

Please tick the series you would like to receive
if you are one of the lucky winners

Presents™ ❑ Enchanted™ ❑ Medical Romance™ ❑
Historical Romance™ ❑ Temptation® ❑

Are you a Reader Service™ Subscriber?   Yes ❑   No ❑

Mrs/Ms/Miss/Mr.......................Initials ....
(BLOCK CAPITALS PLEASE)

Surname ....

Address ....

....

....Postcode ....

(I am over 18 years of age)   C7L

One application per household. Competition open to residents of the UK and Ireland only. You may be mailed with offers from other reputable companies as a result of this application. If you would prefer not to receive such offers, please tick box. ❑

Mills & Boon® is a registered trademark of Harlequin Mills & Boon Limited.